He had everything he wanted. Money. Cars. Women. Power. And Culverwell.

There was on... ...ne thing left ...o make his achievements ... ...ete and that ... was Grace Tyler. She be... ...d he meant to... have her— even without ... ...king him if ...hat was the way it had to ...

But she still ... ...ed him. He'd have to be blind not to ... ...ced that b...traying little flutter in her ... where... ...er he came within touching dist... ...r, the fl...shed cheeks and dilated p... ...n the ...entre of her huge, man-drowni... ...ine eyes. She still wanted him as muc... ...e wanted her—if that were possible—an... ...sn't going to rest until her lovely legs ... ...pped around him again and she was ... beneath hi..., sobbing out his name.

Elizabeth Power wanted to be a writer from a very early age, but it wasn't until she was nearly thirty that she took to writing seriously. Writing is now her life. Travelling ranks very highly among her pleasures, and so many places she has visited have been recreated in her books. Living in England's West Country, Elizabeth likes nothing better than taking walks with her husband along the coast or in the adjoining woods, and enjoying all the wonders that nature has to offer.

FOR REVENGE
OR REDEMPTION?

BY
ELIZABETH POWER

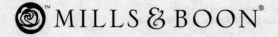

MILLS & BOON

First published in Great Britain 2010
Harlequin Mills & Boon Limited,
Eton House, 18-24 Paradise Road, Richmond, Surrey TW9 1SR

© Elizabeth Power 2010

ISBN: 978 0 263 87840 0

Harlequin Mills & Boon policy is to use papers that are natural, renewable and recyclable products and made from wood grown in sustainable forests. The logging and manufacturing process conform to the legal environmental regulations of the country of origin.

Printed and bound in Spain
by Litografia Rosés, S.A., Barcelona

FOR REVENGE
OR REDEMPTION?

FOR CAROL, SHEILA AND ROY

CHAPTER ONE

'OPENING nights are always nerve-racking, Ms Tyler,' the red-haired young woman with the clipboard told Grace reassuringly, pinning a microphone to the pearl-grey lapel of her designer jacket. 'But this gallery's going to do well. I just know it is!' Her raised eyes skimmed a wall of contemporary paintings, signed prints and ceramics in the tall, glass case immediately behind Grace. 'We're doing the exterior shots first, so you won't be on for a while yet.' She tugged gently at the lapel, running deft fingers over the smooth sheen of the expensive fabric, brushing off a pale strand from Grace's softly swept-up hair. 'There! The camera's going to love you!' the woman enthused.

Which was more than the press did! Grace thought, remembering the hard time they had given her after her split with her fiancé, wealthy banker's son Paul Harringdale, four months ago. Then the tabloid's comments about her had ranged from "butterfly-minded" and "fickle" to "the tall, slinky blonde who wasn't capable of making the right decision if her life depended upon it". It had all been cheap reporting—and the fact that that last remark had come from a journalist who had pursued her romantically without success wasn't worth losing sleep over—but it had hurt nevertheless.

'Good luck,' someone said in passing as the doors opened

and invited guests, critics and members of the art world started pouring in.

'Thanks. I'll need it,' Grace laughed over her shoulder, realising it was her friend, Beth Wilson, a curvaceous and vertically challenged brunette, as she liked to call herself; at four-feet-eleven, she assured everyone that life for her was always looking up. Also loyal and efficient, she was the woman Grace had appointed to run her small London gallery while she carried on with her main objective in life, which was to try to keep afloat the nationally renowned textile company that her grandfather had founded and which had run into serious problems since his death just over a year ago. And with no moral support from Corinne.

Since inheriting her husband's share of the company, Corinne Culverwell had made it clear that she wasn't interested in being actively involved in the business. Now, with showers of congratulations and good wishes seeming to come at her from every angle, Grace darted a glance around her as the launch party got under way, wondering why her stepgrandmother—a name that always seemed inappropriate for a woman who was barely three years older than herself—had claimed that a prior engagement at the last minute prevented her from coming tonight.

Directing two well-wishers to the table where the champagne was being served, Grace noticed the camera crew packing up outside. She had to stay focused, she told herself firmly, steeling herself for the interview that was now imminent. *Stay calm. Relaxed.*

'Hello, Grace.'

A prickling tension stiffened her spine as those two softly spoken words dragged her round to face the man who had uttered them.

Seth Mason! She couldn't speak—couldn't even breathe for a moment.

She would have recognised him from his voice alone, a

deep, rich baritone voice with no trace of any accent. Yet those masculine features—strongly etched and yet tougher-edged in their maturity—were unforgettable too. How often had her dreams been plagued by the stirring images of that hard-boned face, those steel-grey eyes above that rather proud nose? The slightly wavy, thick black hair still curling well over his collar, with those few stray strands that still fell idly across his forehead.

'Seth…' Her voice tailed away in shock. Over the years she had both longed and dreaded to see him again, yet she had never expected that she would. Especially not here. Tonight. When she needed everything to go right for her!

From his superior height, his penetrating gaze locked onto hers and his firm, well-defined mouth—the mouth that had driven her mindless for him as it had covered hers—twisted almost mockingly at her discomfiture.

'How long has it been, Grace? Eight…nine years?'

'I—I don't remember,' she faltered, but she did. Those few fateful meetings with him were engraved on her memory like her five-times table. It had been eight years ago, just after her nineteenth birthday, when she had thought that everything in life was either black or white. That life was mapped out for her in just the way she wanted it to go and that anything she wanted was hers for the taking. But she had learned some hard lessons since then and none more painful than the ones she had suffered from her brief liaison with this man—when she had discovered that nothing could be taken without there being a price, and a very high price, to pay.

'*Don't* remember, or don't want to?' he challenged softly.

Flinching from the reminder of things she didn't want to think about, she took some consolation from realising that they were concealed from most of the party by the tall case of ceramics. She ignored his velvet-sheathed barb and said with a nervous little laugh, 'Well…fancy seeing you here.'

'Fancy.'

'Quite a surprise.'

'I'll bet.'

He was smiling down at her but there was no warmth in those slate-grey eyes. Eyes that were keener, more discerning, if that were possible, than when he'd been…what?… twenty-three? Twenty-four? A quick calculation told her that he would be in his early thirties now.

The tension between them stretched as tight as gut, and in an effort to try and slacken it she tilted her small pointed chin towards a display of watercolours by an up and coming artist and asked, 'Are you interested in modern art?'

'Among other things.'

She didn't rise to his bait. He had an agenda, she was sure, and she wasn't even going to question what it might be.

'Did you just walk in off the street?' His name certainly hadn't been on the guest list. It would have leaped out at her instantly if it had been. Nor was he dressed to kill like a lot of the other guests. He was wearing an open-necked white shirt beneath a leather jacket that did nothing to conceal the breadth of his powerful shoulders, and his long legs were encased in black jeans that showed off a lean waist and narrow hips, a testament to the fact that he exercised regularly and hard.

'Now, that would be rather too much of a coincidence, don't you think?' he supplied silkily, although he didn't enlarge upon how he had managed to cross the threshold of her little gallery, and right at that moment Grace was far too strung up to care.

Making a more obvious point of looking around her this time, she asked, 'Is there anything you fancy?' And could have kicked herself for not choosing her words more carefully when she saw a rather feral smile touch his lips.

'That's a rather leading question, isn't it?' Rose colour deepened along her cheekbones as images, scents and sensations invaded every screaming corner of her mind. 'But I think the answer to that has to be along the lines of once-bitten, twice shy.'

So he was still bearing a grudge for the way she had treated him! It didn't help, telling herself that she probably would be too, had she been in his shoes.

'Have you come here to look around?' Angry sparks deepened her cornflower-blue eyes. 'Or did you come here tonight simply to take pot shots at me?'

He laughed, an action that for a moment, as he lifted his head, showed off the corded strength of his tanned throat and made his features look altogether younger, less harshly etched. 'You make me sound like a sniper.'

'Do I?' *I wonder why*? Grace thought ironically, sensing a lethal energy of purpose behind his composed façade, yet unable to determine exactly what that purpose was.

The dark strands of hair moved against his forehead as he viewed her obliquely. In spite of everything, Grace's fingers burned with an absurd desire to brush them back. 'Still answering every question with a question?'

'It would seem so.' She was amazed that he remembered saying that, even though she hadn't forgotten one moment of those torrid hours she had spent with him. She met his gaze directly now. 'And you?' He'd been a boatyard hand from a poor background, manually skilled, hardworking—and far, far more exciting than any of the young men she'd known in her own social sphere. 'Are you still living in the West Country?' His nod was so slight as to be indiscernible. 'Still messing about with boats?' It was only her nervousness that made it sound so detrimental, but by the way those steely eyes narrowed he'd obviously taken it exactly the wrong way.

'It would seem so,' he drawled, lobbing her words back at her. 'But then, what did you expect from a young man with too many ideas above his station? Wasn't that what you as good as said before you went on to make me look an utter fool?'

She flinched from the reminder of things she had done when she had been too young and wrapped up in herself to know any better.

Defensively she said, 'That was a long time ago.'

'And that excuses your behaviour?'

No, because nothing could, she thought, ashamed, and it was that that made her snap back, 'I wasn't offering excuses.'

'So what are you offering, Grace?'

'You think I owe you something?'

'Don't you?'

'It was eight years ago, for heaven's sake!'

'And you're still the same person. Rich. Spoilt. And totally self-indulgent.' This last remark accompanied a swift, assessing glance around the newly refurbished gallery with its pricey artwork, fine porcelain and tasteful furnishings—which owed more to her own flair for design than to cost. 'And I'm still the poor boy from the wrong side of town.'

'And whose fault's that?' His whole hostile attitude was causing little coils of fear to spiral through her. 'It's hardly mine! And if you persist in this—this—'

'Dissecting of your character?' He smiled, clearly savouring her lack of composure.

'I'll have you thrown off the premises,' she ground out in a low voice, hoping that no one else could hear.

The lifting of a thick eyebrow reminded her of how ridiculous her threat was. His commanding height and solid frame gave him strength and fitness that put him light years ahead of anyone else milling around her little gallery. That oddly feral smile pulled at the corners of his devastating mouth again. 'Going to do it yourself?'

Unwelcome sensations ripped through her as she thought about physically handling him, about the way his hard, warm body had felt beneath her hands: the strength of contoured muscle, the sinewy velvet of his wet skin.

'I didn't think so,' he breathed.

He seemed so confident, so sure of himself, Grace marvelled, wondering what made him think he could just march in here and start flinging insults at her; wondering in turn why he hadn't moved on. He had seemed so ambitious—full of high expectations, determined. And it was that determination to have what he wanted that had made him so exciting to her...

'Why the Mona Lisa smile?' he asked. 'Does it give you some sort of warped satisfaction to know that life didn't turn out the way we thought it would—for either of us?'

Grace lowered her gaze so as not to see the smugness in his eyes. If he thought—quite wrongly—that she'd been mocking him for not amounting to much then he was clearly enjoying reminding her of a future she had taken so much for granted when she had been young and so stupidly naïve.

Trying not to let him get to her, and still wearing a wistful little smile, she uttered, 'Not as much satisfaction as it's clearly given you.'

He dipped his head in an almost gallant gesture. 'Then that makes us even.'

'Really?' She grasped a flute of champagne from the tray of drinks being offered to them, even though she had decided earlier to keep a clear head tonight. She noticed Seth shake his head quickly in silent refusal. 'I hadn't realised we were clocking up a score.'

'Neither did I.' His sensuous mouth curved from some inward amusement. 'Are we?'

The pointed question caught her off-guard and before she could think of a suitable response to fling back he went on. 'I stopped envying you, Grace. And people like you. I never did manage to master the art of using others in my bid to get the things I wanted, but I'm learning,' he told her with scathing assurance. 'Nor did I ever find it necessary to do what was expected of me just to impress my own elite little circle of friends.'

Her interviewer had finished his piece outside with the film crew and was talking to the producer on the pavement. Any minute now he would be in to talk to her.

How must she look? she thought, panicking, feeling totally harrowed after coming face to face with Seth Mason.

'If all you want to do is take out your frustrations and your disappointments on me just because things didn't turn out for you the way you thought they would…' Flushed, uncomfortably sticky, she inhaled deeply, trying to stay calm, stay in control. 'Then you could have chosen a more convenient time to do it! Or was your intention behind coming here tonight simply to unsettle me?'

He smiled, and his face was suddenly a picture of mock innocence. 'Now, why would I want to do that?'

He knew why; they both knew why. She wanted to forget it, but it was obvious that he never had. Nor was he going to, she realised despairingly.

'I was merely interested to see the newsworthy Grace Tyler's new venture for myself, although I understand that it isn't entirely new. I know that you inherited this shop some years ago and only recently had it transformed from a run-down, barely viable concern to this temple of fine art I see before me today.'

It was information he could have got from any sensation-seeking tabloid, Grace realised, but still she didn't enjoy the feeling that he, or anyone, for that matter, knew so much about her.

'Quite a diversion for you from the world of textiles,' he commented. 'But then you showed promise…in an artistic sense…' His marked hesitation told her exactly what he thought about the other traits of her character. 'Eight years ago. Let's hope you have more success with this—' his chin jerked upwards '—than you've had managing Culverwells— or any of your relationships, for that matter.'

Stung by his obvious reference to her recent broken engagement as well as the company's problems, Grace looked up into that hard, cold but oh, so indecently handsome face with her mouth tightening.

Had he come to gloat?

'My relationships don't concern you.' The only way to deal with this man, she decided, was to give back as much as he was giving her. Because it was obvious that a man with such a chip on his shoulder would never forgive her for the way she had treated him, even if she got down on her knees and begged him to, which she had no intention of doing! 'As for my corporate interests, I don't think that's any of your business, either.'

A broad shoulder lifted in a careless shrug. 'It's everyone's business,' he stated, unconcerned by her outburst. 'Your life, both personal and commercial, is public knowledge. And one only has to pick up a newspaper to know that your company's in trouble.'

The media had made a meal of the fact, accusing her and the management team at Culverwells of bringing the problems about, when everyone who wasn't so jaundiced towards her knew that the company was only another unfortunate victim of the economic downturn.

'I hardly think a boat hand from…from the sticks is in a position to advise me on how I should be running my affairs!' She didn't want to say these things to him, to sound so scathing about how he earned his living, but she couldn't help herself; she was goaded into it by his smug and overbearing attitude.

'You're right. It is none of my business.' His smile was one of captivating charm for the redhead with the clipboard who was standing with the gallery manager a few feet away, gingerly indicating to Grace that they were ready to interview her. 'Well, as I said, I wish you success.'

'Thanks,' Grace responded waspishly, aware of that undertone of something in his voice that assured her his wishes were hardly sincere. Even so, she plastered on a smile and crossed over to join her interviewer, wishing she was doing anything but having to face the camera after the unexpectedly tough ordeal of meeting Seth Mason again.

Outside in the cold November air, Seth stopped and watched with narrowed eyes over the display of paintings in the window as Grace faced a journalist who was renowned for making his interviewees sweat.

Smiling that soft, deceptive smile, she appeared cool, controlled and relaxed, answering some question the man asked her, those baby-blue eyes seeming to flummox her interviewer rather than the other way around.

She was as sylph-like as ever, and as beautiful, Seth appreciated, finding it all too easy to allow his gaze to slide over her lovely face, emphasised by her pale, loosely twisted hair, and her gentle curves beneath that flatteringly tailored suit. But she hadn't changed, he thought, as he felt the inevitable hardening of his body, and he warned himself to remember exactly what type of woman she was. She would play with a man's feelings until she was tired of her little game. The way she had dumped him and the last poor fool, her fiancé, was evidence of that. She was also still an unbelievable snob.

What she needed was someone to let her know that she couldn't always have her own way; someone who would demand respect from her, and get it. In short, what she needed was someone who would bring her down a peg or two—and he was going to take immense satisfaction in being the one to do it.

CHAPTER TWO

THE interview was over, and so was the party.

Grace breathed a sigh of relief.

The evening had gone well. In fact, Beth had taken several orders for quite a few of the paintings and sold one or two of the ceramics. The interview, too, had turned out satisfactorily, without her having to face any of the awkward questions she had been dreading. She should have been happy—and she was, she assured herself staunchly, except for that meeting earlier with Seth Mason.

She didn't want to think about it. But as she went upstairs to the flat above the gallery, having locked up for the night, long-buried memories started crowding in around her and she couldn't stop them coming no matter how hard she tried.

It had been shortly after her nineteenth birthday, during the last few weeks of her gap year between leaving college and starting university, when she had first met Seth in that small West Country coastal town.

She'd gone down from London to stay with her grandparents who had brought her up and who had had a summer home there, a modern mansion high in the wooded hills above the little resort.

On that fateful day that would stay for ever in her memory, she'd been out with her grandfather when he had decided to call into the little boatyard on the far side of town. She couldn't even remember why, now. But, while Lance Culverwell had been in the scruffy little office, she had noticed Seth working on the hull of an old boat. She'd noted the way his broad back moved beneath his coarse denim shirt, the sleeves of which had been rolled up, exposing tanned, powerful arms as he'd driven rivets hard into the yielding metal, unconsciously raking back his untameably black hair, strands of which had fallen forward tantalisingly as he worked.

When he turned around, she looked quickly away, though not in time for him to fail to register where her gaze was resting on the hard, lean angles of his denim-clad hips.

He didn't say anything. He didn't even acknowledge her presence with a smile. But there was something so brooding in those steely-grey eyes as she chanced another glance in his direction that she felt herself grow hot with sensations she'd never experienced before just from a man looking at her. It was as though he could see through her red crop-top and virginal-white trousers to the wisp of fine lace that pushed up her suddenly sensitised breasts, and to her skimpy string, the satin triangle of which began to feel damp from more than just the heat of the day.

The faintest smile tugged at one corner of his mouth— a sexy mouth, she instantly decided, like his eyes, and the prominent jut of his rather arrogant-looking jaw. She didn't acknowledge him, though, and wondered whether to or not. But then Lance Culverwell came out of the office with the owner of the boatyard, and she gave her smile to the two older men instead.

She didn't look back as she walked over to the long, convertible Mercedes that was parked, top down, the gleaming silver on the gravel like a statement of her family's position in life beside the older, far more modest vehicles that were parked there. Instinctively, though, she knew that his eyes were following her retreating figure, the way her hair cascaded down her back like a golden waterfall, and the not entirely involuntary sway of her hips as she prayed she wouldn't miss her footing in her high-heeled sandals all the way back to the car. She even begged Lance Culverwell to let her drive, and she pulled out of that tired-looking little boatyard with her head high and her hair blowing in the breeze, laughing a little too brightly at some remark her grandfather made, wanting to get herself noticed—wanted—and by *him*.

He wasn't right for her, of course. He was a mere boat hand, after all, and far removed from the professional type of young men she usually dated. But something had happened between her and that gorgeous hunk she'd exchanged glances with that day, something that defied cultural and financial differences, and the boundaries of class and status. It was something primeval and wholly animal that made her drive back from town in a fever of excitement, guessing that Lance Culverwell would be appalled if he knew what she was thinking, feeling—which was an overwhelming desire to see that paragon of masculinity who had made her so aware of herself as a woman again, and soon.

She didn't have long to wait. It was the following week, after she had been shopping in town.

Laden with purchases for a party her grandparents were giving, she was just starting up the hill, wishing she hadn't decided to walk down that morning but had brought her car instead, when one of her carrier bags suddenly slipped out of her hand just as she was crossing the road.

Making a lunge for it, and dropping another bag in the process, she sucked in a breath as a motorbike suddenly cruised to a halt in front of her and a black-booted foot nudged the first errant carrier to the side of the carriageway.

'Hello again.' The sexily curving mouth of the leather-clad figure on the bike was unmistakable: Seth Mason. She remembered her grandfather casually referring to him on the way home the previous week, and had hugged the name to her like a guilty secret. Her heart seemed to go into free fall as he spoke to her, then felt like it was beating out of control.

'You've bitten off more than you can chew.' He looked amused at her plight. His voice, though, was deep and so warm that she fell in love with it just standing there on that rural road as he bent to pick up the one bag she still hadn't retrieved and restored it to her flustered arms. 'You look as though you could do with a lift.'

Every instinct of survival screamed at Grace to refuse, to listen to the nagging little voice of wisdom that warned her that involving herself with this man would definitely be biting off more than she could chew! But everything about him was exciting, from his dark, enigmatic features to his hard, lean body and the heavy pulsing of the motorbike's engine between those powerful, leather-clad thighs.

'I'm Seth Mason...if you're wondering,' he stated dryly, after she deposited her bags in the pannier and sat astride the bike.

'I know,' she said, easing down her mini-skirt that had ridden up to reveal more golden thigh than she wanted him to see.

'Aren't you going to tell me your name?' A distinct edge crept into his voice as he added, 'Or do you think I should know it?'

Grace had laughed at that. 'Don't you?' she asked cheekily.

From the look he sent over his shoulder, he wasn't particularly impressed.

'I'm Grace,' she told him quickly in the light of his challenging, brooding gaze.

'Here.' He thrust a crash helmet into her hand. 'Put this on.'

'Do I have to?'

'If you want to ride with me, you do.'

He was responsible for her safety, that was what he was

saying. The thought of having his protection sent a little frisson through Grace.

Somewhat nervously she said, 'I've never been on a motorbike before.'

'Then hold on to me,' was his firm command.

Even now, letting herself into the flat, Grace could still remember the thrill of putting her arms around his hard, masculine body. Of laying her cheek against the warm leather that spanned his back while the bike had throbbed and vibrated like a live thing beneath them.

'Lean when I do!' he shouted back above the engine's sudden roar. 'Don't pull against me.'

Never in a million years! the young Grace sighed inwardly, utterly enthralled, though she kept her feelings to herself for the unusually lengthy journey home.

'You took the long way round.' She pretended to chastise him, stepping off the bike. Her legs felt like jelly and for more reasons than just the vibration, or the speed with which he had driven the powerful machine along a particularly fast stretch of road.

Something tugged at the corners of his mouth. 'Well, they do say a girl always remembers her first time.'

Her cheeks felt as though they were on fire as she took off her helmet and handed it back to him. 'I will. It was truly unforgettable. Thanks.' But her voice shook at the images his comment about a girl's first time gave rise to. What would he say, she wondered, if he knew that there never *had* been a first time in that most basic of respects? That she was still a virgin? Would he lose interest in her? Because she was sure there was interest there. Or would he regard her as a challenge, like a lot of the men she'd dated had, backing off when they'd realised she wasn't an easy lay?

He was looking at the impressive security gates, and the big house with its curving drive visible behind them, but as she moved to retrieve her purchases from the pannier he said, 'Would you like a hand carrying those in?'

Setting the electric gates in motion, she laughed, saying, 'I don't think that's really necessary, do you?' But then, impelled by something outside her usually reserved nature, she was shocked to hear herself adding provocatively, 'Or do you?'

It was a game she had been playing with him; she knew that now—in hindsight. Now that she had the benefit of maturity on her side. But she had wanted him, so badly, even while she'd known that a relationship with a man like Seth Mason was strictly taboo.

She cringed now as she thought about her behaviour at that time. Even so, she couldn't stop the memories from spilling over into every nook and cranny of her consciousness, no matter how much she wanted to hold them at bay.

'Exactly what do you want from me, Grace?'

She remembered those words like they'd been spoken yesterday as, helmet removed, he'd come round to the rear of the bike and helped recover the last of her bags.

She took it from him with a hooked finger, laughing, but nervously this time. 'Who says I want anything from you?'

He studied her long and hard, those penetrating grey eyes so disquieting that she was the first one to break eye-contact. Distinctly she remembered now how vividly blue the sky had been behind his gleaming ebony head, and how the colours of the busy Lizzies in the borders along her grandparents' drive had dazzled her eyes almost painfully with their brilliance as she averted her gaze from his unsettling regard.

'You know where to find me,' he drawled, turning away from her with almost marked indifference, so that she felt deflated as she moved along the drive.

The starting up of his bike was an explosion of sound that ripped through the air and which brought her round to see only the back of his arrogant figure as he shot off like an avenging angel down the long, steep hill. The roar of his engine seemed to stamp his personality on every brick and balcony of the quiet, prestigious neighbourhood, and seemed to linger long after he had gone.

She didn't go down to the boatyard again. She couldn't bring herself to be so totally brazen as to let him think she was actually chasing him, even though it was torture for her not to make some feeble excuse to her grandparents and sneak down into town to see him.

In fact it was completely by accident when she met him again. With her grandparents visiting friends farther afield for a couple of days, she was out walking alone, exploring the more secluded coves along the coast.

Climbing over a jutting promontory of rocks, she clambered down onto the shingle of a small deserted beach some way from the town. Deserted, except for Seth Mason.

On the opposite side of the beach, wearing a white T-shirt and cut-off jeans, he was crouching down, his back turned to her, doing something to the lowered sail of a small wooden dinghy.

Grace's first instinct was to turn and head quickly and quietly back in the direction she had come from, but in her haste she slipped, and it was the crunch of her sandals on the shingle as she fought for her balance that succeeded in giving her away.

He looked round, getting to his feet, while she could only stand there taking in his muscular torso beneath the straining fabric of his T-shirt and the latent strength of his powerful, hair-covered limbs.

'Are you going to join me?' he called across to her, sounding unsurprised to see her there, as if he had been expecting her. 'Or are you just a vision designed to lure unsuspecting sailors into the sea?'

She laughed then, moving towards him, her awkwardness easing. 'Like Lorelei?'

'Yes. Like Lorelei.' He was watching her approach with studied appreciation. 'Have you been sent here simply to bring about my destruction?'

She laughed again, but more self-consciously this time, because his masculine gaze was moving disconcertingly over the soft gold of her shoulders above her strapless red top, travelling all the way down to her long golden legs exposed by what she suddenly considered were far-too-short white shorts. 'Why do you say that?'

'Didn't she have a song so sweet it could make any man lose his course?'

She wondered if he was applying that analogy to her, and knew a small thrill in guessing that he probably was.

'And do you have one, Seth Mason?'

He turned back to the dinghy perched on its trailer, and started to hoist the sail, checking something in the rigging. With a hand shielding her eyes from the sun, Grace watched the breeze tugging at the small orange triangle.

'Do I have a what?'

Turning her attention to the bunching muscles in those powerful arms, she said, 'A course.'

Solid and purposeful, his work taking all of his attention, he didn't say anything until he'd drawn the small sail down again.

'Why,' he enquired suddenly, turning back to her, 'does everything you say sound like a challenge?'

She remembered being puzzled by his remark. 'Does it?'

'And why do you answer every question with a question?'

'Do I?' she'd exclaimed, and then realised what she'd said and burst out laughing.

As he laughed with her it seemed to change his whole personality from one of dark, brooding excitement to one of devastating charm.

Caught in the snare of his masculinity, she could only gaze

up at his tanned and rugged features; at the amusement in those sharp, discerning eyes; at those strong, white teeth and that wide, oh, so sexy mouth. Madly she wondered how that mouth would feel covering, pressing down on, plundering hers.

'Do you do anything else but mess about with boats?' Her voice cracked as she asked it. In her heady state she wondered if he might have guessed at the way she was feeling and wondered, mortified, if he might take her question as another kind of come-on, because where he was concerned she couldn't seem to help herself.

'That's about the size of it.' His tone reverted to that familiarly curt and non-communicative way he had of answering her, like he was challenging her to criticise all he did—the person he was.

She walked round to the other side of the dinghy. 'Is this one yours?'

A hard satisfaction lit his face at that. 'She's not worth much.' Lovingly he ran a hand over the boat's smooth contours, a long, tanned hand that had Grace speculating at how it might caress a woman's body. 'But she delivers what she promises.'

She sent him an oblique glance. 'And what's that?' she quizzed, wondering instantly why she had asked it.

Heavy-lidded eyes fringed by thick, black eyelashes swept over her scantily clad body, and there was a sensual curve to the hard, masculine mouth as he uttered in a deeply caressing tone, 'Just pure pleasure.'

And he wasn't just talking about sailing his boat! There was a sexual tension between them that screamed for release, unacknowledged but as tangible as the hard shingle beneath her feet and the sun that played across her face and bare shoulders.

To break the dangerous spell that threatened to lead her into a situation she didn't know how to handle, she searched desperately for something to say. Remembering his reference to the sea-nymph, earlier and deciding that there was much more to him than she could possibly guess at, without thinking she found herself suddenly babbling, 'Where did you study the romantic writers?'

'I didn't.' He started pushing the boat towards the water's edge. 'Not everyone's lucky enough to go to university.' She wondered if that remark was a dig at her, and her family's wealth and position, but she let it go. 'I have a widowed mother.' Foster mother, as it had turned out. 'And foster siblings to support.' The boat was down in the water then, released from its support, bobbing on the gentle waves. 'I pick things up.'

Nothing would escape him, Grace decided, before he said, dismissing the subject, 'Right. She's ready.' He was holding the rope that was still attached to the trailer. 'Do you like the water?' he threw back over his shoulder. 'Or would it be another first for you if I took you out for a spin around the bay?'

'Are you asking me?' Her heart had started to beat like crazy.

'Is that a yes?'

She nodded, too excited because he'd asked her to say anything else. But quickly, as he leaped into the boat, she slipped off her sandals and started wading in.

'You're right, this is a first. I've never been in a dinghy before,' she gabbled, too conscious of the callused warmth of the hand he extended to help her, although she couldn't avoid adding with a provocative little smile as she was climbing in, 'My grandparents have a yacht.'

Suddenly she was being yanked down so forcefully beside him that she gave a little scream as the boat rocked precariously, and she had to make a grab for the soft fabric of his T-shirt to steady herself.

'Now why doesn't that surprise me?' he drawled.

Caught for a moment in the circle of his arms, aware of the deep contours of his chest and the heavy thunder of his heart beneath, she thought that he was going to kiss her as he dipped his head.

Instead, with his lashes coming down to hide any emotion in those steel-grey eyes, he said, 'Take the rudder while I get the sail up,' before moving away from her, leaving her fiercely and inexplicably disappointed.

It was an unforgettable afternoon. They sailed until the sun began to dip towards the sea while they seemed to talk about nothing and everything. She learned about his background—how he had never known his father and how he had been given up by his mother when he was three years old; about the orphanages he'd lived in and the foster homes. He had been with the family he was living with now, he told her, since he was fifteen. Now they were *his* responsibility, he stated with a surprising degree of pride. Just as they had made him theirs in the beginning.

He reminded her of how she had asked him earlier if he had a course, and he told her of his interest in architecture and his intention one day to build a new house for his foster mother. Marina-side, he said. With a view of boats from every balcony.

She laughed at that and said, 'All yours, of course!'

He didn't share her laughter, lost as he was in his personal fantasy. 'I think I'll put it there,' he speculated, pointing to the piece of derelict industrial wasteland where the tall chimneys of a disused power-station created a blot on the landscape.

'There?' She frowned, wrinkling her nose in distaste. 'I don't think she'd thank you for that!' She laughed again.

'And what about you? Do you have a dream, Grace?' His tone was slightly off-hand as though he didn't think too much of her making fun of his dreams. 'Or do you have so much that there's nothing left worth striving for?'

'No. Of course not!' she stated indignantly. 'I intend to settle down. Marry.'

'What—some ex-public-school type that Daddy's vetted who'll give you two-point-five children and a houseful of business associates to entertain?'

She didn't tell him that her father didn't figure in her life, that he'd given up his paternal duties after she'd caused her mother's death simply by being born. Those things were too private—too personal—to share with a total stranger, however handsome or amazingly sexy he might be.

Instead, guessing that it was mere envy that made him speak so derisively of her future, she asked, 'And what's wrong with that?'

'And that's all you intend to do?'

'No,' she argued, wondering why he made it sound so mundane, unromantic, as she watched him lowering the sail. 'There's the company. I'm earmarked to follow in my grand-father's footsteps one day.'

'Ah, yes, the company. And that's it—cut and dried? With no deviating from the pre-arranged course, no surprises, no dreams of your own?'

'Dreams are for people who crave things they haven't a hope of ever attaining,' she stated, feeling a little piqued. 'We inhabit different worlds. In mine the future's carved out for us, and that's the way I like it.'

'Suit yourself,' he said dismissively, giving all his attention then to securing a rope around a mooring buoy, while Grace had been glad to let the subject drop.

A little later, when he was leaning back relaxing for a few minutes with his face to the sun, she took a small sketch-pad from the big silver beach-bag she'd brought out with her that morning and drew a cormorant sitting on a rock drying its outstretched wings in the early-evening sun.

'You're good. You're very good,' Seth praised over her shoulder, making her clasp the drawing to her, warmed by his compliment, but suddenly terribly self-conscious at her efforts.

'You're too talented to be embarrassed about it. Let me see,' he insisted, but in reaching for her pad his fingers accidentally brushed the soft outer swell of her breast beneath her top, and it was that which had put the spark to the powder keg waiting to blow.

'Would you care for a swim?' His voice was suddenly thickened by desire, the grey eyes holding hers communicating a message that was as sensual as the feelings that were raging through her.

'I—I don't have any swimwear,' she responded, excitement coiling in her stomach.

His mouth compressed wryly. 'Neither do I.'

She looked away from him, suddenly nervous as she'd laid down her sketch pad. 'OK. But turn around.'

He laughed, but did as she requested, while she made short work of stepping out of her shorts and pulling her red bandeau-top over her head.

Without looking at him, she stepped nimbly out of the boat and plunged into the sea, gasping from the unexpected coldness of the water.

Coming up for air some way from the dinghy, she heard the deep plunge of Seth's body breaking the surface of the water just behind her.

They were moored near a small cove with a beckoning crescent of soft golden sand. Above and around it rose the sheer rugged face of the cliffs, making the small beach inaccessible to anyone without a boat.

Scrambling ashore first, Grace stood there on the wet sand in nothing but her flesh-coloured string, wondering how she could feel so free, so uninhibited. What she hadn't reckoned on was the impact of Seth's masculinity as he emerged from the water, hair plastered to his head, rivulets cascading over his hair-coarsened chest and powerful limbs; he was like some marauding sea-god, bronze from head to toe and unashamedly potent in his glorious nakedness.

None of the men Grace knew would have dared to walk naked like this, and she could only stand there and let her eyes feast on the sheer perfection of his body.

She should have crossed her arms over her own nakedness, turned away, but it didn't even occur to her—and anyway, she couldn't have torn her eyes away from him even if she'd wanted to.

Instead, raising her arms, she slipped her hands under the wet sheet of her hair, lifted it up and let her head tip back, revelling in the proud glory of her femininity.

She knew how she would look to him with her body at full stretch, the opposite to everything he was. Her long legs were silky and golden, her flat stomach smooth between the gently curving bowl of her hips and her breasts high and full, their sensitive tips hardening into tight buds from the excitement of all that she was inviting.

He came up to her and she lifted her head, her blue eyes beneath her long, wet lashes slumberous with desire, a desire such as she had never known before.

He didn't say a word and Grace gasped from the wet warmth of the arm that was suddenly circling her midriff, pulling her against him. The damp matt of his chest hair was a delight against her swollen nipples; he was already erect, and she'd felt the thrusting strength of his manhood against her abdomen.

His breath was warm against her face as his other hand shaped its oval structure; his fingers, first tender, then turning into a hard demand as they capped the back of her head, tilting her mouth upward to accept the burning invasion of his.

His hands moved over her with such possessive mastery that she became like a wild thing in his arms, her pleasure heightening out of control, as he slid down her body to take first one and then the other of her heavy, throbbing breasts into his mouth.

There was no need for words. She scarcely knew him, but she didn't need to know any more. From that first instant when their eyes had met in that boatyard, she had known instinctively that he was destined to be the master of her body. And when he peeled off her wet string and laid her down on the sand, positioning himself above her, she knew that every glance, every word and every measured sentence that had passed between them since they met had all been a prelude to this moment—the moment when he pushed through the last boundary and the taboo that separated them to claim the surprisingly painless gift of her virginity.

It had all been her own fault, Grace thought now as she went through into her rather bijou kitchen to fix herself some supper, berating herself, as she had done so many times over the years, for the way she had encouraged him. But as she filled her kettle, reached into the fridge and took out a carton of milk, some cheese and margarine, then hunted around for her tin of crackers, she knew that she hadn't had it in her power to stop it happening.

Her lower abdomen tightened almost painfully as she recalled how tender a lover Seth Mason had been even then, as a very young man—which led her to the reluctant speculation of just how experienced he would be now, until she realised what she was doing.

Did she care? He might be married, for all she knew. And, even if he were, what was it to her? Now? After all these years?

Finding the crackers, she started to spread margarine over one of the small discs with such vehemence that it split in several places, sending a shower of brittle crumbs across the worktop.

A mild little curse escaped her as she went to grab a piece of kitchen roll and dampen it under the tap.

What she had felt for Seth Mason had been crazy and totally irrational, a teenager's crush on someone who merely excited her because she knew her family wouldn't approve. Forbidden fruit—wasn't that what they called it? Her brows knitted in painful reverie as she began mopping up crumbs from the work top.

In spite of that, though, she had made a date with him for the following evening, arranging to meet on the beach where his boat was kept, because her grandparents were back by then and she had strictly forbidden him to pick her up from the house.

But she had forgotten the dinner party that she had been expected to attend with her grandparents that evening, which she hadn't been able to get out of, and she'd had no way of contacting Seth without anyone finding out. She'd forgotten to get his mobile-phone number, and she hadn't been able to ring him at the boatyard as she'd learned that the owner— his boss—and her grandfather were old friends. So she had broken their date without a word—no message of regret, no apology. Which would have been rude enough, she thought, straightening up and dropping the soiled kitchen-paper into the bin, without that final blow to his ego.

The following day she had seen him again when she'd gone down to town with her grandfather and Fiona, the daughter of a neighbour just a couple of years older than Grace who had elected to come with them.

Having left her grandfather at the newsagent's, Grace was walking along the high Street with Fiona when she suddenly looked up and saw Seth coming out of a shop.

Seth saw her too, and started to close the few yards between them, but then he held back, waiting for her to make the first move. She noticed the burning question in his eyes: *where were you last night?* No one with half an eye could have mistaken his smouldering desire for her that he made no attempt to hide.

A flame leaped in her from the memory of their mutual passion, of his hard hands on her body and the thrusting power of his maleness as he had driven her to a mind-blowing orgasm. But panic leaped with it, along with shame and fear of anyone finding out that she'd been associating with him and telling her grandfather. Fiona Petherington was a terrible gossip, as well as the biggest of snobs. 'Look at the way that boy's looking at you!' she'd remarked witheringly. 'Who is he? Do you know him?'

'Oh, *him*,' Grace remembered answering, as coolly as she was able to. 'Just some boat boy who's been sniffing round me. Quite sexy, if you don't mind slumming it.' Then she'd cut him dead and walked straight past him—and as she passed she realised from the look on his face that he'd overheard.

The memory of her behaviour that day still made her cringe. But she had paid for it less than ten minutes later. Having left her snobbish companion talking to two other neighbours that they had bumped into outside the chemist's, she popped across the road to the bank. She didn't know whether Seth had followed her or not but as she came out of the building he was striding up the steps outside.

She could still feel the angry bite of his fingers around her wrist as he drew level with her, could still see the condemnation in those angry eyes.

'Slumming it, were you? Is that what you thought you were doing with me down there in the sand?' It was a harsh demand, but low enough so that anyone passing couldn't hear. 'You think you're so high and mighty, don't you?' he breathed when she struggled free without answering, shockingly aware of Lance Culverwell coming up the steps to meet her. 'Well, go ahead, have your five minutes of amusement. But don't think that anything we did on that beach was for any other reason than because I knew I could!'

Those words still lacerated her as much as they had then, even though at the time she had known she deserved them.

Making love with him had been so incredible for her that, crazily, even after her shameful treatment of him, she'd wanted to believe that they had been incredible for him, too.

But Lance Culverwell had had his suspicions about what had gone on. His interrogation had been relentless, and there had been rows back at the house. The following morning she had been packed off to London with her grandmother and she had never seen Seth again. Until today.

Pushing back the plate of crackers and cheese that she suddenly had no appetite for, she tried telling herself not to think about Seth Mason, to forget about him altogether. She hadn't seen him in eight years before he had turned up at the gallery this evening, so there was no reason why she was ever likely to see him again.

Yes, she'd acted abominably, Grace admitted, but that was before she'd learned that pleasure, however fleeting, had to be paid for. Because six weeks after their uninhibited passion on that beach she had discovered that she was pregnant. That she was having Seth's baby. Seth Mason, who wasn't good enough even to be seen out with in her and her family's opinion, was going to be the father of her child!

CHAPTER THREE

'WHAT do you have to say about the dawn raid on Culverwells, Ms Tyler?' A microphone was thrust in her face and cameras flashed in a bid to capture the slim young blonde in the scooped-necked black t-shirt, combat trousers and trainers whose arm, draped with a casual jacket, was already reaching out to the revolving door.

'No comment.' She'd come straight in from New York and she couldn't deal with the press now, not while she was tired, jet-lagged and wondering what the hell had been going on while she had been away. She would deal with them later, she decided, when she had had a chance to speak to Corinne. But her grandfather's widow hadn't been answering her calls, either at home or on her mobile. Grace knew that the only way anything could have happened to Culverwells was if Corinne had been behind it.

'Surely you must have some statement to make? There will be changes in management—redundancies—surely?'

'I said, no comment.'

'But you can't really think…?'

Their persistent questions were mercifully cut off by the revolving door. She was inside the modern, air-conditioned building, the head office of the company that still bore her grandfather's name, even though it was in public ownership.

The silver-haired, moustached features of Lance Culverwell gazed down at her from the huge framed portrait in the plush reception area and, grabbing a moment to steady herself, Grace gazed back at it with tears of anger and frustration biting behind her eyes.

Oh, Granddad! What have you done?

It had been a shock to everyone when he had died last year and left everything he had, including his company shares, to his bride of two years. Not that Grace had begrudged Corinne anything; she'd been Lance Culverwell's wife, after all. But her grandfather had been so smitten by the ex-model that he couldn't have—or wouldn't have— even contemplated anything like this happening, Grace thought despairingly.

A *dawn raid*, that journalist outside had called the takeover, giving rise to a picture in Grace's mind of masked men on horseback brandishing rifles, intent on plundering the company's safe.

If only it were that simple! she thought giddily, clutching her bum bag—which was the only piece of luggage she hadn't instructed the taxi driver to drop off at her flat—as she took the executive lift to the top floor.

'Grace! I tried and tried to reach you…' The portly figure of Casey Strong, her marketing manager, rushed forward to meet Grace before she had barely stepped out of the lift. Grey-haired and due for retirement any day, he was flushed and out of breath. 'Your phone was off.'

'I've been in the air!' She had come straight from the airport, having spent most of her time in New York trying to persuade one of their best customers not to take their business away from Culverwells. It was a PR job that hadn't yet produced the result she wanted, as the company's governing body was taking time to consider what its future action would be.

'Grace! You're here at last!' It was Simone Phillips, her PA, who knew the problems that Culverwells was facing as well as anyone. It was the middle-aged, matronly Simone, who had finally managed to get hold of her with the shocking news of the takeover just as Grace had been coming through customs.

'It's Corinne. She's sold out!' the woman declared, confirming Grace's worst suspicions. 'And so has Paul Harringdale—your ex.' Paul had had a big enough stake in the company to give him and Grace an equal share with Corinne. Which was why Lance Culverwell had probably thought his company would be in safe hands and his granddaughter well provided-for, Grace realised bitterly; he would never have dreamed she would terminate her engagement as she had amidst a good deal of adverse publicity.

'We've got a new CEO, and there's already talk of a massive shake-up in upper management so he can get his own board up and running, like, *yesterday*!' she told Grace dramatically. 'The only up side is that he's gorgeous and single, which means he's probably as ruthless as hell and will probably be ousting us all at the first opportunity!'

'Over my dead body!' Grace resolved aloud, pushing wide the door to the board room which had been standing ajar. To meet a sea of new faces all swivelling in her direction as her fighting words intruded on something the new CEO had been saying.

'If that's the way you want it,' a deep voice, ominously familiar, told her from the far end of the table. 'But it's usually my method to do these things without anyone's actual blood on my hands.'

As the tall, impeccably dressed man in the dark suit and immaculate white shirt stood up, Grace's mouth dropped open.

Seth Mason!

'Hello again, Grace.' His deep, calm tones only emphasised the vortex of confusion that her mind had suddenly become.

It *was* Seth Mason. But how could it be? How could he have made the leap from a boat-fitter, or whatever he had been, to this international business-mogul? Because that was what Simone had called the man who had taken over when she had reached Grace so desperately on her mobile phone just after she'd stepped off that plane. And there was no doubt that Seth was the new CEO.

'Do you two know each other?' Grace wasn't sure where the question came from, only half aware that one or two of the older men had risen to their feet when they had realised who she was. She could feel everyone's eyes skimming over her crumpled and totally inappropriate clothes.

The dynamo at the opposite end of the table raised an eyebrow in mocking query. He was waiting for her response, which she was too dumbfounded to give.

'Oh, I think Ms Tyler will tell you—we way back.'

She was still standing there near the door, unable to think properly, unable to speak; her only coherent thought was that Corinne obviously hadn't had the courage to speak to her until Grace had found out for herself what had happened.

'Can I have a word with you?' She couldn't believe how squeaky her voice sounded.

The subtle lift of a broad shoulder was the action of a man who couldn't be fazed. 'Fire away.'

In private, her eyes demanded.

The new man in charge glanced around at the others members of his team.

'Would you excuse us?' There was no disputing the depth of command in Seth Mason's voice.

Chair legs scraped over the polished floor as everyone complied. To Grace it seemed like for ever before they had all filed out.

'You had something you wanted to say?' he prompted when the door closed behind the last of them, leaving her alone with him in the room where all the major decisions were made.

Yes, she did, she had a lot to say to him! But his smouldering sexuality was something she hadn't reckoned on being so disturbed by, now that there was no one else around.

Images swam before her eyes of the way he had been eight years ago—of the feel of warm leather as he'd drawn her back against him where she'd sat astride that bike; of the warmth of his breath on her throat as one sure, strong hand had slid up to cup her breast, already too sensitive from his attentions...

'Why didn't you tell me?' she challenged angrily, dumping her jacket and bag down on the table and trying not to let his raw masculinity affect her. 'You must have known about this two weeks ago, that night you turned up at my gallery! Why didn't you say anything about this then?'

'And spoil the surprise?'

Of course. That was the whole point of takeovers like this—so the company being taken over wouldn't have time to organise any opposition to it. Grace gritted her teeth, her breathing shallow, breasts rising and falling sharply beneath her T-shirt.

'You led me to believe...' That he was still working in that boatyard. That he was...She couldn't think clearly enough to remember exactly what he had said. 'You let me think...'

'I did nothing of the sort,' he denied coldly. 'You jumped to your own conclusions with that discriminating little brain of yours.' A humourless smile curved his mouth as he came around the long table. 'What is it they say about giving someone enough rope?'

Grace raked her fingers agitatedly through her hair. It must look a mess—*she* looked a mess, she thought, standing there like a street urchin in her own boardroom. The hasty clean-up she had managed in the cramped washroom on the plane did nothing to make her feel adequately groomed beside his impeccable image.

'Well, you've come a long way, haven't you?'

'Not nearly far enough yet. Not by a long chalk.' Hostility seemed to emanate from every immaculately clothed pore.

'What do you mean?' Grace challenged, eyeing him warily.

He uttered a soft laugh. 'I mean I've waited a long time for this moment, and I intend savouring every satisfying minute.'

Unconsciously, she moistened her lips. 'Is that what this takeover's all about? Revenge?'

He laughed again, a harsh, curt sound this time. 'I prefer to call it making the most of one's opportunities.'

'What? Vindictively buying up enough shares so that you could steal my grandfather's company from under my nose?'

'Vindictive? Possibly. But not *stolen*, Grace, *acquired*— and quite legitimately. And hardly from under your nose. You've been enjoying yourself in New York for the past week or so, I understand, so you can hardly expect a man in my position not to salvage the spoils when you go off designer shopping—or whatever it is a woman like you does alone in the Big Apple—while your ship is sinking.'

'I didn't desert. And Culverwells isn't sinking.' *If only it wasn't!* she thought despairingly. *Nor was I 'designer shopping'!* she wanted to fling at him. But she decided that it wouldn't be worth the time or the effort, any more than it would be to tell him that she had sorely needed any free time she might have had in New York, as it was the first real break she had taken in the past eighteen months. 'OK. We'd hit a slump. But we would have pulled ourselves out of it eventually. We were surviving.'

'A pity your shareholders didn't share your confidence. It's clearly that bury-your-head-in-the-sand attitude that has put Culverwells into the state it's in today. Or have you been too busy with your rich boyfriends and your fancy little gallery that you didn't recognise disaster when you saw it?'

There was a glass of water on the table by the note pad in front of a vacated chair, the back of which she hadn't realised she was clutching. She had to restrain the strongest urge to pick the glass up and fling the contents right into his smug and incredibly handsome face.

'Don't even think about it,' he warned softly, disconcertingly aware.

'I've never buried my head in the sand. None of us has!' she retaliated fiercely, ignoring his pointed reference to the company she kept. 'It's been down to global forces and the dropping off of sales because the market's been depressed. It still grates, doesn't it? That I was born to all this when you—you were…'

'What? Not good enough to tread the same ground you walked on?'

'I didn't say that.'

'You didn't have to.'

No, she had made her opinion of him quite clear with those disparaging comments she hadn't meant him to hear before simply ignoring him in the street!

She couldn't deal with thinking about that right now. In fact, she could only deal with the shame of it by tossing back, 'So you think my team and I are just going to lie down while you sit at that table, lording it over us and throwing your weight around?'

'I don't actually care what you do, Grace,' he assured her, his body lean and hard as he moved purposefully towards her, as hard as those grey eyes that didn't leave hers for a second. 'And may I remind you that there was a time—however short—when my weight wasn't something you were totally averse to?'

A rush of heat coursed through Grace's veins, bringing hot colour up over her throat into her cheeks. Unbidden, those images surfaced again, and she saw him as he had been on that beach, those long fingers marked with grease as he'd worked on his dinghy. She smelled the salt of the sea air, felt the sun's warmth caress her skin, and then felt the thrill of that hard, masculine body pressing her down, down into the sand.

'That was a mistake,' she said shakily.

'You're darn right it was. On both our parts. But, as the saying goes, None of our mistakes need ever be permanent.'

'Meaning?' He was so close now that her breath seemed to lock in her lungs.

'Meaning you taught me a lot, Grace. I should be eternally grateful to you.'

'For what?'

'For showing me exactly how to handle women like you.'

A sharp emotion sliced through her, piercing and unexpected. Evenly, though, she said, 'You don't intimidate me, Seth, if that's what you're trying to do. And, as for salving that macho ego of yours, I think you managed that quite adequately eight years ago.'

Grace wasn't sure if he needed to be reminded, but those heavy eyelids drooped and a cleft deepened between those amazing eyes.

Seth felt momentarily uncomfortable at the reminder of having said something that, even then, was beneath his usual code of ethics. He couldn't even remember the exact words he had used, only that they had been a flaying retaliation for the way she had treated him.

'Yes, well…' He was regaining his cool, reclaiming the upper hand—which was what he needed to do, he reminded himself, with this calculating little madam. 'No man appreciates being snubbed by someone who only forty-eight hours before was sobbing with the pleasure of having him inside her.'

A deep throb made itself felt way down in her lower body. Surely she couldn't still be attracted to a man who with one swoop had just seized all that her grandfather had worked for—and whose only motive, where she was concerned, was to seek revenge?

'So this is how it's going to be.' His abrupt return to business put her off-balance to say the least, before he went on to give her a brief résumé of his plans for Culverwell's. 'I shan't make any unnecessary redundancies, unless I see areas of overstaffing or anything that will be detrimental long-term to the company and its other employees if I desist. I'll keep you on as my assistant—I can't deny that your expertise in the field of textiles will be invaluable. If you co-operate and accept my leadership, you won't have anything to worry about where your job is concerned. If you don't…'

'You'll have me fired, right?'

He didn't affirm or deny that statement. His narrowing eyes, though, resembled hard chips of steel, and harsh lines suddenly bracketed his mouth.

'Like your grandfather was instrumental in doing to me?'

Grace frowned. 'What are you talking about? You didn't work for my grandfather.'

'Directly, no, but he had interests in that boatyard, and enough clout with its owner to see that I was swiftly dispatched for even daring to breathe on his precious granddaughter, let alone lay my rough, rude hands on her supposedly chaste little body.'

His derision at the kind of girl he thought she was stung more than she wanted to admit. He didn't know she'd been a virgin. It had all been so easy; how could he have known?

'I—I didn't know.' She was shaking her head now in horrified rejection at Lance Culverwell ever stooping to do what Seth was accusing him of—and because of her. 'Really, I didn't.' But it would explain Seth's driving motive all these years, she realised—to get even with her family.

'Is that contrition I see in your eyes, Grace? Surely not! It really doesn't become you.'

'Why? Because you think I'm not capable of any feeling?' Surprisingly, the notion that he could even consider that cut deep—but it was just her pride that hurt, she convinced herself. Nothing else. 'Anyway…' Her reluctant gaze swept over the thick, black hair, which even an expensive cut hadn't altogether tamed, over the designer suit and exclusive black shoes. Ignoring the sudden quickening of her heart-rate that just looking at him produced, she said waspishly, 'It doesn't seem to have hurt you any.'

'Not so much as my mother who was already struggling to make ends meet. But, hey! What's a man's job when you live in a nice, comfortable mansion with more food than you could ever eat and servants to fetch and carry for you at the snap of your fingers?' His hostility and resentment burned in him like an eternal flame. 'And you complain that I think you aren't capable of any feelings? I'm quite sure that you and your kind don't have any regrets about trampling on others to get what you want, particularly those worse off than yourself.'

She flinched from his continual need to verbally flay her.

'You don't know *my kind*, Seth Mason. You haven't the first idea what sort of woman I am.'

'Haven't I?' he grated. 'Then all the more reason why I should keep you around to discover this new Grace Tyler for myself—and I think it's going to be a very enlightening journey.'

'Get lost!'

'As much as you'd like that, Grace, I'm afraid that this time that isn't going to happen. I'm calling the shots now. Take it or leave it, but I don't think you'll walk away with your tail between your legs like a disciplined little lap-dog because you're way too proud and you've got far too much to lose. No. You'll take it, and, before I've finished with you, lying down!'

His innuendo was obvious. But he had her just where he wanted her, she realised, because as he had already made clear he knew she'd stick it out. It was the only way she would have any say in, or be able to hang on to, even a part of all that her grandfather had spent his life working for, she thought. She despaired at how the woman he had been so besotted by could have thrown her on the mercy of a man like Seth Mason. Nevertheless, that pride that he had spoken off a moment ago had her flinging back recklessly, 'You reckon?'

'Don't present me with a challenge, Grace. I think it only fair to tell you that I thrive on them.' Which was obvious, she thought, shuddering from the determination in him, otherwise he wouldn't have got to where he was today.

'That's big of you,' she retorted, knowing she was playing with fire but unable to let him have the last word. 'Well, let me tell you, I haven't worked my butt off getting where I have in this firm to be walked over by an arrogant, overbearing, jumped-up boatyard worker from the back of beyond! I'll work alongside you for the sake of the company, but let's get one thing clear—you might have pulled yourself up out of the next best thing to the gutter...' Angrily, she snatched up her jacket and bag. 'But you'll never, *ever*, get me into bed with you again!'

The walls seemed to shake as she slammed the boardroom door behind her.

'Wow! What, already? He's a fast worker!' That dry comment from Simone, who was just coming along the corridor, fell onto the deafening silence that followed.

'That isn't funny, Simone.' Hot and shaking from her outburst, Grace felt uncomfortably sticky beneath her travel-creased clothes.

'No, I can't say amusement was the overriding emotion coming out of that boardroom. Care to tell me where you know him from?'

'No.'

Her PA pulled a knowing face. 'That memorable, was it?'

'I'm sorry, Simone,' Grace apologised, not meaning to have spoken so sharply to her assistant. 'I guess I'm suffering from a chronic case of jet lag.' She shook her head to try and clear it. 'Among other things,' she exhaled, her eyes swivelling towards the room she had just so dramatically vacated. She couldn't believe that this wasn't some farcical nightmare that she would wake up from any minute. An inner anguish pleated her forehead as she tagged on, 'It was a long time ago.'

'Not long enough for him to bring out a side of your nature I've never seen—or heard.' This with a roll of her eyes towards the ceiling. 'Are you all right? Can I get you something?'

'Yes. Enough Culverwell shares to give me a majority holding.' *So that I won't lose all that was precious to my grandfather—to me—to a man hell-bent on revenge!*

Simone grimaced sympathetically. 'No can do, girl. I think all we can do is co-operate with him and the new management and pray that we've still got jobs this time next week.'

'How can I co-operate—?' The boardroom door suddenly opening left Grace's words hanging in mid-sentence.

Seth Mason emerged, appearing more dynamic and commanding in the narrower confines of the corridor, if that were possible. He sent Grace a stripping glance. She had been way too rude in there, and something told her he wasn't going to let her get away with it.

'Simone, I'd like you to bring your note pad in here. But first will you have a word with whoever it is you need to see about having self-closing hinges fitted on all principal doors?'

'Certainly, Mr Mason,' Simone responded with what seemed to Grace like annoying deference to the new CEO, before she caught the covert glance her assistant sent her. It conveyed the message already obvious from Seth's instructions; *he isn't going to take anyone slamming doors in his face!*

'I see,' she said, rounding on him as the other woman tripped off towards the lift. 'So she's your PA now, is she?'

'No,' he surprised her by answering, 'But I thought you wouldn't mind my making use of her until my own arrives.'

'It so happens, I do mind. And no one *makes use* of anyone in this company,' she enlightened him, piqued by the dismissive manner in which he had just spoken about a member of her team. 'I just thought I ought to warn you, otherwise you might wonder why you've got a full-blown mutiny on your hands.'

'Thanks for the warning.' He smiled indolently, making her body react to him in a way that made her brain chastise her for her stupidity. 'It was just a figure of speech. Why don't you go home, Grace?' Strangely, his tone had softened, become dangerously caressing in its sensuality. She had a feeling that it was some sort of mind game he was playing with her. 'Grab a couple of hours' sleep? Freshen up a bit?' His gaze raked with disconcerting thoroughness over her dishevelled appearance. 'We've got a lot of work to do and I'm sure you'll agree that no one can give their best if they aren't functioning on all cylinders.'

Was that concern in his eyes? she wondered, then dismissed the notion, deciding that it was probably pity. The type one would have for an animal one has just snared as one mulled over the most humane way to make the kill.

'Perhaps you'd prefer it if I didn't come back at all!' Her fighting spirit rose to her defence, challenging him.

'On the contrary,' he said, and this time his mouth curved in a fragment of a smile that did nothing to warm his eyes, just merely showed her how calm he was in contrast. 'As I've already explained, I'm going to spend every satisfying minute working with you.'

Don't imagine it will be a bed of roses! It took every gram of will power Grace had to bite the words back. This was her family's business, in name if nothing else, and she'd be darned if she would let Seth Mason goad her into throwing in her share and just walking away, as Corinne had done, or give him any reason to get rid of her which—unbelievable and humiliating though it was—he now had the power to do.

'You're right,' she accepted, deciding to ignore his last remark that made her blood pump heavily through her with its scarcely concealed implication. Her head was pounding too and she was longing for a shower. 'I think I will freshen up.'

But she didn't summon a taxi to take her home.

No way, she decided, was she going to take the advice of this conceited, over-confident, muscle-bound boat builder—or whatever he had been—and abandon her staff just when they needed someone to reassure them that all their hard work and their loyalty wasn't just going to be written off.

Instead, swinging away from him, she took the lift down to her own office. This time when she rang the Culverwell home, Corinne answered.

'How could you?' Grace breathed as the much-too-affected voice of her grandfather's widow started trying to placate her with some hollow, meaningless explanation. 'How could you? And without breathing a word of it to me?'

'Because I knew you'd react like this.' Corinne sounded irritated. Grace could almost see her sitting at her marble-topped dressing table in her transparent negligee, her short red hair gelled to look as though she'd just tumbled out of bed, a cooling mask on her face as she applied precise sweeping strokes of lacquer to her perfect nails. 'Be sensible, Grace.

I wanted to sell my shares—so did Paul—and you couldn't afford to buy them.'

'Paul?' The fact that her ex could have been complicit in trying to oust her from the board of the family company made her wonder if there was something going on between him and Corinne. 'Did you cook this up between you?'

'No, we didn't. I haven't seen Paul Harringdale since you broke up with him. He's not my type.'

No. Your type is more besotted elderly men who'll give you anything just to hear you flatter their diminishing egos! Grace thought bitterly.

'When you've calmed down a bit, Grace, you'll realise that I've done Culverwells a favour. The company needs a man like Seth Mason. When he approached me to see if I'd sell, what could I do? He can be pretty persuasive. Wow! I don't know what you're complaining about. I can't imagine it being that much of a punishment, taking orders from a man like that.'

Grace bit back the desire to tell her grandfather's widow that she could go ahead and take orders from him if she wanted to, because *she* wasn't going to. But then she would have to hand in her resignation and she had already promised herself that she wouldn't do that.

'Goodbye, Corinne.'

Ringing off, she stepped through into the adjacent shower-room and, stripping off her clothes, stepped under the refreshing spray of the jets, wishing she could cut off her thoughts as easily as she had cut the line to her grandfather's widow.

But the memories wouldn't leave her alone, and unwillingly she found herself reflecting on the emotional chaos of eight years ago: the shock of her pregnancy. Her shame and regret over the way she had behaved. The unbelievable anguish following a miscarriage at four-and-a-half months.

It was then that she'd realised that life wasn't just one big party; that there were debts to be paid and rules to be respected, and that some things in life had a far, far greater value than status or money.

But she didn't want to think about any of that. It was all because of seeing Seth again that the past had opened its floodgates, making her dwell on things that she wanted, needed, to forget: regret. Loneliness. Self-blame. The pain of her loss.

She didn't have to think about it, and she wouldn't, she told herself fiercely. She had enough worries with the company right now and the shock of Seth Mason taking over.

Towelling herself off, she went through into the dressing-room adjacent to her office and, sliding back the doors on the mirror-fronted cupboards, she scanned the shelves for fresh underwear. She always kept a change of clothes in the office in case of an unexpected out-of-hours meeting or dinner when she couldn't get home to change.

Now she pulled a silver-grey silk blouse and dark business-suit down off their hangers, donned clean underwear and drew a short pencil-line skirt up over her hips.

She couldn't, wouldn't, let him get to her, she determined as she slipped on her blouse and came through into her office to jot down a reminder to herself of a dental appointment that had almost slipped her mind. She couldn't help wondering what he would say if he ever found out that there had been repercussions from their love-making all those years ago. What he would think—that it had been her comeuppance for the appalling way in which she had behaved?

Fumbling with the top fastening of her blouse, she shuddered from the thought of how he might gloat. She was glad that he didn't know and would never know all that she had been through. Then she looked up, startled, her eyes dark and enormous, to see him striding into her office.

'Don't you ever knock?' she challenged, flustered, still trying to fasten her blouse which was gaping open, revealing too much of her creamy breasts in their black lacy cups.

'The door was open.' He looked as shocked and surprised

as she was to see him, while his eyes skimmed with barely veiled masculine interest over her state of undress. 'Anyway, I thought you'd gone home.'

'Because you ordered me to?' She couldn't seem to give him any leeway, even if she wanted to.

'Advised,' he corrected. 'Not ordered.'

'And leave my customers and all the people who depended on my grandfather and now me in the hands of…of…'

'The enemy?' he supplied mockingly when she couldn't think of a word strong enough to describe him.

She chose to ignore his remark and his coldly sardonic smile, relieved that she had finally managed to slip the top button of her blouse securely into place.

'What did you want?' she demanded, more ungraciously than she had intended, because the way he was looking at her made every betraying little cell in her body react to him in a way she wasn't at all happy about.

'The last five years' trading figures. Perhaps you could look them out for me, since you're here.'

She swept over to the desk, jotting down the appointment in her diary with hands that shook. 'Perhaps you could look them out for yourself since you've obviously given yourself licence to everything else in this building.'

'Not quite everything, Grace.' The way his eyes swept over her body needed no interpretation. 'Not yet.'

She stood facing him, trembling with anger and frustration at his audacity. How could he even think he could say such things to her, let alone imagine that she would gladly leap into his bed? Though she was certain most women would. But, while she was battling to find a suitably cutting response, he said, clearly aware, 'Are you going to fight me every step of the way?'

It was suddenly painful to swallow. Pulling herself up to her full height, which in her stocking-clad feet still left her well short of his six-feet-plus inches, she replied, 'If I have to.'

'That isn't very sensible.'

'Well, no. We both know I'm rather lacking in that department, don't we? Or, rather, I used to be,' she tagged on pointedly. One thing she had learnt from that encounter with him was wisdom, if nothing else.

'Really?' A masculine eyebrow cocked in disdainful speculation. 'And I've always believed I was the one lacking judgement in that regard.'

His tone, with his opinion of the fickle creature she had been, still had the power to flay. But if he thought making love to her had been an error of judgement on his part, then it must have meant something more to him than just a feather in his cap, as he'd claimed that day outside the bank, mustn't it? Grace reasoned wildly. She did not want to dwell on the fact that it was only her actions, and subsequently her grandfather's in getting Seth dismissed from his job, that had fuelled his determination to make the Culverwells pay.

'I think it only fair to warn you, Grace,' he said, his next words emphasising that determination, 'That if you continue to fight me then it'll be a fight you're going to lose. I can turn this company's fortunes around or I can break up Culverwell's piece by piece and sell off the most profitable areas at considerable loss to yourself and all those people you claim so depend on you. It's your choice.'

There was no point arguing with him. He was clearly wealthy and powerful enough to do exactly as he said by stripping the company of its assets. And where would she—and a lot of people who would lose their jobs because of it—be then?

Walking purposefully over to the bank of cabinets on the far wall, she opened a drawer and pulled out the file he had requested before propelling the usually smooth-gliding drawer back hard on its runners.

'There.' Ignoring the masculine hand waiting to take it

from her, she tossed the heavy file down onto the desk in front of him. 'Is there anything else you'll be requiring…*sir*?'

Thick black lashes came down over steely eyes as he moved to pick up the file. 'Just for you to control your temper,' he said. 'Much as I'm not wholly averse to a fiery nature in a woman, I much prefer it if she keeps such loss of control confined to bed.'

'That's just the sort of sexist comment I'd expect from you,' she flung at his broad back, because he was already heading for the door.

He turned as he reached it, his immaculately clad free arm lifting to the doorjamb. He was the hard-hitting executive, all flippancy gone.

'I've called an emergency meeting of all the major shareholders at two o'clock this afternoon. If you care as much about this company as you say you do, you'll be there.'

Then he was gone, leaving her staring after him in angry frustration, a knot of tension tightening way down inside her from his remark about being in bed.

Seth leaned back against the mirrored wall and closed his eyes as the lift doors came together behind him.

She'd looked so bleak in there when he had surprised her walking into that office, almost hollow-eyed, he thought. He wondered if there was more behind that lovely face and body of hers than just a fear of losing the lifestyle she was clearly used to if he took it on himself to get rid of her. Perhaps she had changed from the spoilt little rich bitch it had been his misfortune to get involved with, the girl he'd often read about with interest in the tabloid press. She had seemed genuinely shocked when he had told her how Lance Culverwell had been responsible for him losing his job.

But don't be fooled, he warned himself, in danger of finding himself being charmed by her femininity. She would eat a man for breakfast and spit him out again without turning a hair.

He couldn't help wondering, if he was honest with himself, if he hadn't seduced her all those years ago just to prove something to himself, as he'd let her believe. But, no; she had been utterly desirable. Just thinking about her then, and being faced with the reality of just how beautiful and even more desirable she was now, made him realise that he had never wanted anyone so much as he'd wanted Grace Tyler—then or now!

Over the years he had managed to achieve everything he had set out to and that he had worked for. His architectural studies had made him a natural in a profession he had striven to reach, a lucky break had taken him into full-blown developments and now he had everything he wanted: Money. Cars. Women. Power. And Culverwells. There was only one thing left to make his achievements complete and that was Grace Tyler. She belonged in his bed, whether she liked it or not. And he meant to have her—with or without her liking him, if that was the way it had to be.

But she still wanted him. He'd have had to be blind not to notice that betraying little flutter in her throat whenever he came within touching distance of her, the flushed cheeks and dilated pupils in the centre of her huge, man-drowning blue eyes. She still wanted him, as much as he wanted her —if that were possible—and he wasn't going to rest until her lovely legs were wrapped around him again and she was lying there beneath him, sobbing out his name.

CHAPTER FOUR

THE little art gallery was peaceful and soothing on Grace's
jangling nerves now that Beth had closed up for the day and
gone home; Grace needed peace as much as she needed some
sleep after a day doing battle with the likes of Seth Mason.

Left to her unexpectedly four years ago by the father she'd
scarcely known, the gallery had been a run-down little shop
selling artists' materials, and had come with a sitting tenant
in the flat above and a whole load of debt.

Never a fan of Matthew Tylers' for abandoning his daughter as he had, Lance Culverwell had urged Grace to give it
up.

'It will only bring you heartache, child,' she could still hear
her grandfather saying. 'Which is all that man ever brought
you while he was alive.'

But something deep down inside Grace hadn't been able to
let the gallery go and, refusing any help from her grandfather,
she had started to pay the outstanding mortgage herself. Which
had seemed quite feasible until Culverwell's had started getting into difficulty. Then her grandfather had died, leaving
everything to Corinne, and Grace had been forced to give up
the bright, modern apartment she had been buying and move
into the rather dowdy and suddenly vacant flat above the gallery in a much more modest part of town.

Struggling to meet the cost of her planned refurbishments

for the flat and gallery, she'd looked like losing both. But her father's paintings, virtually unnoticed while he had been alive, had already started to gain unexpected popularity, as had his sculptures, several of which Grace had seen change hands in various auction houses for surprisingly high prices over the past couple of years. But it had been that one special bronze of Matthew Tyler's that had brought all her fears for her gallery to an end, helping her to clear her debts and carry out her renovations after it had sold to a telephone bidder and fetched a mind-blowing sum.

So, even if Seth Mason had taken Culverwells from under her nose, at least this gallery was hers, she thought fiercely, looking around at the fine paintings and ceramics. Lock, stock and barrel!

The fact that she had had to part with what the art world claimed was her father's prize piece to achieve it brought on those familiar feelings of regret, as well as a whole heap of conflicting emotions whenever she thought about her father.

With tears threatening to sting her eyes, she tried to banish any sentimental feelings towards Matthew Tyler from her mind.

Just looking at that little figurine had always made her feel sad—and angry too—hadn't it? she assured herself. Anyway, she'd had to sell it to stay solvent, and that was that.

The phone was ringing in the flat as she started up the stairs.

Exhausted from the day, she considered leaving the answering machine to take the call, but as it hadn't cut in by the time she crossed the lounge she picked the phone up, then wished she hadn't when Seth's deep tones came disconcertingly down the line.

'Just checking that you're in and planning on an early night,' he remarked with that infuriating audacity that had Grace instantly snapping back.

'No, as a matter of fact I thought I'd pop up to the West End, take in a show and then do a bit of clubbing for a few hours. I'm tired, jet-lagged and, if you hadn't noticed, my grandfather's company was taken over today! A company that's been in my family for over fifty years!' The emotion she had managed to rein in downstairs now welled up in her again, clogging her throat, making her voice crack from the struggle she was having to keep it in check. 'Of course I'm getting an early night. I'm not quite as robotic as you obviously expect your workforce to be.'

'Or as well, by the sound of it. You sound distinctly nasal,' he commented, much to Grace's alarm. She couldn't—wouldn't—let him know that it was taking every resource she had not to break down after the day she had had. 'You aren't sickening for anything, are you? A cold, perhaps?'

'As if you'd care!' She had slammed the phone down before she even realised what she was doing, and stood there, staring at it, shaking with rage.

How dared he? How dared he try to control her private life as well as her business affairs? she fumed as she continued to stare at the phone, both apprehensive and fired up, waiting for it to start ringing again.

Relieved when it didn't, yet feeling strangely as though she'd been left hanging by ending their conversation in the way she had, she went back across the tastefully though minimally furnished living room, kicking off her high-heeled shoes as she did so. They weren't designed for a day in the office any more than her trainers would have gone with the executive image she had been particularly keen to cultivate today. But her pumps had been in the suitcase which she'd instructed the taxi driver to bring on to the flat this morning in her haste to get to the office.

Now, going into the bedroom, she slipped off her clothes, pulled her hair free of its pins and was just reaching for the champagne-tinted robe she'd tossed down onto the bed when the bleeper in the hall announced that there was someone at the front door.

'Who is it?' she asked into the loud speaker, shrugging into her robe. She didn't feel up to seeing anyone tonight.

'Seth. Seth Mason.'

Grace's heart instantly lurched into a thumping tattoo. Had he just been round the corner when he'd phoned? 'What do you want?'

'Can I come up?'

She wanted to say no, but her tongue seemed to cleave to the roof of her mouth, and before she was fully aware of what she was doing she was pressing the button that opened the door to the street.

Hearing his steady tread on the stairs, Grace couldn't get over how her hands were shaking as she fumbled with the belt of her robe, only just managing to secure it as those footsteps stopped outside the door to her flat.

'What do you want? she demanded, wondering how he could look as fresh and vital as he had that morning, while stepping backwards to admit him since his dominating figure promised to quash any refusal to do so.

Surprisingly, he was bringing her suitcase up from the passageway. She'd been too tired to bother carrying it up tonight.

'I thought you'd had a pretty tough day.' Pushing the door closed behind him, he stooped to put the suitcase down in the little hallway, his cologne drifting disturbingly towards her. 'I felt something of a peace offering might be in order.' It was only then, as he straightened up, that her brain registered the bouquet of predominantly white-and-yellow flowers he was holding.

'Where did you get these?' She wasn't ready to be placated as he handed them to her. 'Late-night shop at the supermarket?' And instantly she regretted her caustic and rather childish remark when he made no reply.

The bouquet was fragrant and beautifully arranged and the name of an exclusive florist on the wrapping caused her eyebrows to lift in surprise.

Had he been planning to come round with these much earlier? Was that why he had telephoned just now—to check that he wasn't going to have a wasted journey?

'You think that this makes everything all right?' she uttered waspishly. 'That I'll be bowled over by an apology and a few expensive flowers?'

'I'm not trying to bowl you over.' His tone was self-assured, his jaw cast in iron. 'And it certainly isn't intended as an apology.'

Of course not. She laughed. 'No. How stupid of me,' she bit out, swinging away from him into the lounge.

'Why is it,' he asked, following her, his voice suddenly dangerously seductive, 'that when I'm around you you're always in a state of undress?'

An insidious heat crept along her skin, making her heart beat faster, her nerve-endings tingle.

Why? Grace similarly wondered and, caught in the snare of his regard, felt that same throb of tension that she'd felt from the very first instant their eyes had clashed eight years ago.

'Perhaps because I didn't invite you up here in the first place,' she returned heatedly.

Seth's mouth curved in an indolent smile. His senses absorbed the translucent quality of her skin; those blue eyes that could make a man drown in his own longing for her; that rather proud nose that mirrored her attitude towards her subordinates and made him want to drag her to her knees; that full, slightly pouting mouth. He wanted to taste that mouth until he was drugged by the potency of all it promised him, devour it with his own until she was begging him to take her as she had all those years before.

He saw her as she had been then, naked except for that

web of lace across her pelvis, offering herself to him like a beautiful, abandoned spirit of the sea. He had never known a girl as passionate as she had been, although he'd known enough in his time. When he had dropped her off the bike outside her grandparents' house that night, she'd seemed to leap at his suggestion to meet him the following day. He'd felt sick to the stomach when she hadn't turned up, although he'd waited for hours on that beach. And the day after that, when he had bumped into her in town, she'd treated him like he hadn't existed. No, worse—like he was scum. He had been just someone with whom to amuse herself, he thought with his mouth hardening. Just a substitute until she could get back to her richer, stuck-up friends back home.

For a long time afterwards all he could think of was of getting his own back—having his revenge on the Culverwell family for the humiliation they had caused him, and for the hardship they had inflicted on his mother and his foster siblings as a result. Well, now he had, he thought grimly. And it wasn't over yet!

He noted the way she was clutching the flowers to her breast as though to conceal the fact that she wasn't wearing a bra. But he could see that all too clearly from the way her nipples protruded tantalisingly through the satin robe, and he had to clench his fingers to control the urge to rip it from her body and replace it with his aching hands instead.

'You had your hair cut,' he commented with an unaccustomed dryness in his throat, thinking, as he had done when he had seen her again in the flesh that morning, that the mid-length silky cloud that gently brushed her shoulders added a sophistication that hadn't been there eight years ago.

Poignantly she said, 'I grew up.'

And how, he thought. Feeling the uncomfortable constriction of his clothes below waist level, he was annoyed at how she could still affect him without even trying.

'Why have you come?' she demanded, but Seth noticed that

those eyes he had drowned in all too willingly eight years ago were wary, as though she were afraid of him—or, amazingly, herself.

'I was naturally concerned,' he said against his better judgement. She had sounded ghastly over the phone. Now he could see the dark circles under her eyes that no amount of make-up could conceal. She had to be tired, and she was most certainly jet-lagged. But there was something else. Something that caused that same bleak look about her that he had noticed when he had strode into her office that morning, which surprisingly had caused a slight pricking of his conscience, making him feel less a conquering hero and more like a heel for what he had done. 'I thought I'd come and see for myself that you were all right.'

Grace wanted to respond with some cutting jibe, but the events of the day had taken their toll. She had no more energy left to fight him tonight.

'Well, now you've seen me,' she murmured with her shoulders slumping, the bouquet hanging heavily at her side. She felt fit to drop, and as she made to move away from him she tripped over one of the shoes she had left lying on the carpet and would have stumbled if he hadn't been there, reaching for her.

'I don't need your help,' she said despite herself as his long, tanned hands pressed her down onto the sofa, disposing of the flowers on the table beside it.

'Well, that's just too bad, because you're getting it.'

His forcefulness, his proximity and his pine-scented cologne made her weak with a heady excitement that quickly turned to panic when he came down beside her on the settee.

'Who invited you to sit down?' she croaked, breathless from the force with which her heart was thumping.

'Your good manners,' he drawled, half-amused.

His droll remark would have drawn some retort from her if

she hadn't been so keyed up, debilitated by the hot sensations that were pulsing through her.

Desperate to distance herself from him, she was all for leaping up.

As if he could read her mind, though, his arm suddenly sliced across her middle, preventing her precipitous flight.

Grace's gasped breath seemed to lodge in her lungs, every part of her burning with the fire that strong arm was igniting in her as its warmth penetrated the fine material of her robe. His other arm was stretched across the back of the settee, setting her head spinning in a whirl of fear and wild anticipation.

If he kissed her...!

Surprisingly, though, he made no other move to touch her beyond keeping her there.

Rigid with tension, her breasts rising and falling sharply, she breathed, 'What do you want from me, Seth?'

She caught his sharp intake of breath and wondered if that arm lying across her could feel the hard pulse that was throbbing away inside her.

'I believe I once asked the same question of you.'

Yes, he had, she remembered, recoiling from the reminder, because they both knew what it was she had wanted—and, heaven help her, still wanted—from him. In spite of the ruthlessness in his desire for revenge, in spite of all he had taken from her, because she couldn't deny it now.

Sexually, she was as attracted to him as she had ever been. More so, if that was possible. But it was just her flesh that was weak. It meant nothing beyond that, and she had to keep reminding herself of that. Seth Mason was a dangerous man and she'd be a fool if she were to allow herself to fall into his honey-tongued trap. Because that was all it was, she decided—the flowers. The apparent concern. Just ways of wearing her resistance down until he could claim the ultimate prize for himself: her surrender to his powerful sexuality. And what then? she wondered, shuddering.

She longed to put a safe distance between them, and common sense alone prevented her from making any sudden moves. That would have had the same effect as a mouse trying to escape the clutches of a prowling jungle cat, she realised hopelessly, knowing by instinct alone that if she attempted it then that arm would tighten mercilessly around her—and where would she be then?

Instead, her fine features ravaged by her darkest emotions and the things that she must never, ever tell him, and with her eyes fixed on a pastoral watercolour on the far wall that she had bought for next to nothing at a car-boot sale, she asked, 'Just how much persuasion did it take on your part to get Corinne to hand over her share of the company?'

'What is it you want me to say, Grace?' He inhaled deeply, sitting back, mercifully withdrawing his arm as he did so. 'That I'm sleeping with her?'

Unable to help herself, she sent a swift glance towards his hard-hewn face, breathing normally again now that he had released her, or as normally as it was possible to breathe in his devastating sphere. 'Are you?'

His lashes came down, veiling the perfect clarity of his eyes. 'You think I'd kiss and tell on any woman I bed?'

She laughed, a humourless sound strung with tension, as images of him naked on that beach, and as he would be in bed now—his long limbs entwined with others that were paler, more submissive in their passion—rose to threaten her far-too-vulnerable defences. 'Are you trying to tell me you have scruples?'

Seth's mouth compressed. 'No more than you.'

She turned away from him, her chin lifting in spite of the reminder. A cold feeling seemed to settle right in the place where his arm had lain.

'Does it matter to you, Grace?'

'What?'

'Whether I'm sleeping with her or not?'

'Hardly,' she sneered.

He laughed softly, the warmth of his breath stirring the fine hairs at her temple, making her stiffen. 'Such protestation!' he mocked. 'I just wonder why the lady deems it necessary to deliver it with such force.'

'I would have thought that was obvious.' She leaped up now, dreading that she might have given him cause to suspect how her body reacted to him against her will, against her rational thinking. 'You're despicable!' she breathed.

His mouth moved carelessly. 'Shouldn't you be saying that to those closer to home?'

He meant Corinne—and Paul.

Turning wounded eyes in his direction, she noticed the grace with which he moved, brought his tall, lithe frame to his feet.

'She sold you down the river, Grace.' His words were hard, blunt, unsparing. 'So did your precious Harringdale.'

'He isn't *mine*,' she flared, hurting, wondering how he—how both of them—could have pulled the plug on her and left her and the company to the mercy of a man like Seth Mason. 'It's over between us—as you so subtly pointed out at that launch party. It was over months ago.'

'Ah, yes. What really happened there? Did you just get tired of him?' he asked, sounding bored suddenly, while ignoring her barbed accusation. 'Or were you as butterfly-minded and fickle as Harringdale said you were? What was it?' His thick brows pleated as he pretended to search for the words which were obviously at the forefront of that shrewd, keen mind. '"Grace Tyler's only interested in having fun and when that wears off, which is surprisingly quickly, so does her sense of loyalty".' His mouth compressed. After all, hadn't he been on the receiving end of what could only be described as her capricious behaviour? Perhaps he did have reason to think badly of her, she accepted painfully. But that was all in the past.

'I don't think my relationship with Paul is any of your business,' she murmured, catching her breath after the hurtful remarks her ex-fiancé had made to the press when she had broken off their engagement only a few weeks before their wedding. Wearily, she added, 'Perhaps you're just too influenced by what you read.'

'Perhaps,' he concurred, without sounding wholly convinced. 'Perhaps Harringdale was just being spiteful, in view of the way you jilted him. Or perhaps he was right. Perhaps loyalty and respect are two things you still need to learn.'

His words had an ominous ring to them. 'Believe that if you want to,' she objected, so tense that she flinched as the clock on the mantelpiece suddenly struck the half hour. 'Just like every sensation-seeking journalist I've come across, you've got your own prejudiced opinions and nothing I say will change them.'

'Try me.'

'Why?'

He didn't answer, but his eyes were so commanding in their intensity that she found the words slipping away from her before she could stop them.

'If you must know, it was something I drifted into with Paul as much as anything else. I thought we had a lot in common, so it seemed like a good idea for the two of us to get engaged and to merge our business interests. It was what both our families wanted, my grandfather in particular.' She couldn't forget the hints Lance Culverwell had dropped, the silent but eternal pressure he'd applied to see her settle down with the heir to the Harringdale fortune.

'And, with dear Granddad out of the way, you didn't have to.'

'No, strange though this may seem to you, I consider principles to be more important than doing something just because it's expected of me.'

'Really?' Dark, winged brows lifted mockingly. 'And when did you first cultivate that admirable virtue?'

'You can scoff all you like. It's true.'

'And your stepmother?'

'Step-*grand*mother,' she corrected with emphasis.

The look he sliced her left no doubt that he had picked up on that unintentional censure in her voice, and his mouth pulled at one corner, as though he were weighing up the age difference between the ex-model Corinne Phelps and Lance Culverwell, questioning the whole viability of the match.

'It's peculiar how sex drives a man—or a woman, for that matter—isn't it, Grace?'

She regarded him warily. 'Meaning?'

'Meaning he wasn't prepared for someone from my background to soil the pedigree of his precious family, but he had no such qualms when it came to himself and a woman who didn't mind being photographed in some of the more, shall we say, *graphic* newspapers.'

'What my grandfather found out *after* they were married had no bearing on his judgement. And we aren't all like you, Seth Mason. My grandfather didn't marry Corinne for…' She couldn't even bring herself to say it, hating having to listen to someone else voicing the doubts about Lance Culverwell's good judgement that she had harboured in silence, alone. 'He married her because he was lonely.'

Those steely eyes seemed to strip her to the soul. 'If you believe that, then you still haven't grown up, Grace, despite all your claims to the contrary. He might have advocated high standards and good breeding—which he obviously found in the woman he spent most of his life with—but at the end of his life he was no more immune than any other man to the wiles of a pretty gold-digger who has about as much refinement as a bag of raw cane-sugar.'

'Coming from someone as basic as you, that's rich!' she

shot back, hating him for saying these things to her. 'All I can say to that is that it takes one to know one.'

From the anger that flared in his eyes, she realised she had hit a raw nerve.

Scared by the fury she had provoked, she started to move away, but he was too quick for her, and she gave a helpless little cry as he caught her, dragging her into his arms.

Her robe had slipped off one shoulder and, tugging it off the other so that her arms were trapped inside it, he pulled her towards him before his mouth came down hard on hers.

She struggled in his grasp, protesting little sounds coming from her captured lips, but her wriggling only made him more determined, his mouth growing more insistent in its demands.

Her fruitless movements caused her robe to separate. She could feel the rasp of his suit against her stomach, her thighs, her naked breasts.

She groaned again, only this time it was the muted sound of desire. She hated him and yet she wanted him! How sick was that?

The revelation shocked her even as she realised that he had recognised it too.

In response his arms came around her, pulling her into the hard warmth of his body, his mouth leaving hers only to force her head back for his teeth to graze with humiliating purpose over the far too sensitive column of her throat.

Sensations ripped through her such as she had never known for eight long years. Why him? she asked herself savagely, clenching her teeth against all that he was doing to her. Was he destined to be the only man that she could ever respond to?

Hating herself for her weakness, fingers curling tensely against the shoulders of his jacket, she battled with the traitorous responses of her own body so that she was standing breathless and trembling with her eyes closed when he finally lifted his head.

His face was flushed, his mouth taut from the desire he was holding in check, but his eyes were unmistakably smug.

Even so, he seemed to have a struggle drawing breath before he said in a voice that was softly mocking, 'Where are those principles now, Grace?'

'You bastard.' Her lashes parted to reveal the self-loathing in her eyes. 'Was that why you came here tonight?' she demanded shakily, pulling out of his grasp. 'To try to humiliate me?' Her hands were trembling so much she could scarcely do up her robe.

'If it's of any consolation to you, Grace, humiliating you wasn't my intention.'

'No? Exactly what did you intend? To try and soft-soap me with your supposed concern for my welfare, and hope that that and a few well-chosen flowers would have me falling at your feet?'

'Just let me remind you, Grace, that there were two of us involved in that kiss—and *you* responded to *me*. As for my takeover of Culverwells, one day you might just thank me for stepping in when I did.'

'Never!'

'Never say never,' he ridiculed. 'So, we can do this the easy way by being civil and trying to get on…'

'Giving in to your assaults, you mean?'

'Or we can go on just the way we're going,' he said, ignoring her remark, 'And keep up this pointless war. It makes little difference to me.'

'You started it,' she said, and couldn't help cringing at how childish that sounded even to her own ears.

'Oh, no. You began it, my love.' The endearment made its mark, but only because he spoke with such lethal softness. 'Way, way before I'd done anything to earn your contempt.'

'But now you have earned it, so will you just please leave?'

Stooping to pick up his car keys, he didn't stay to argue, only turning as he reached her sitting-room door.

'Get an early night. We've got a lot of work ahead of us,' he informed her with all the blandness of an employer to a subordinate.

A couple of seconds later she heard him close the hall door after him. Biting back tears of frustration, Grace spotted the flowers still lying on the table and, picking them up, hurled them across the room in the direction that he had gone.

CHAPTER FIVE

SETH wasn't in when Grace arrived at the office the following morning and she couldn't have been more relieved.

After all her protestations yesterday about not winding up in bed with him, it had taken only one kiss from him to show her that, where he was concerned, she had no more control over her physical responses than she did over the weather.

As she slipped off her jacket, hung it over the coat stand and then tried to settle down to work she wondered—just as she had done until she'd fallen into a heavy slumber the previous night—she wondered why she had responded to him so disgracefully. Why, when his only interest in her was to seek revenge?

Was it because all her emotions had been so highly charged yesterday—because she had been shattered from a sleepless overnight flight, even before she had suffered the shock of Culverwells being taken over? Or was it simply because she had no resistance whatsoever where Seth Mason was concerned, and that nature—or whatever one could call it, she thought witheringly—would try its utmost to get them into bed whenever they were alone together?

She groaned to herself as she opened her post, staring down at a letter she had unfolded and reading it without digesting a word.

She was still the same woman who had got into that taxi

yesterday morning, determined to fight Culverwells' new CEO for all she was worth, wasn't she? So, she might have played right into his hands and made a total fool of herself, but she still had her fighting spirit and her determination to do what was right for the company.

When the internal phone on her desk buzzed, though, and Seth's deep voice came over the line insisting that she came up to his office, Grace's heart started to pound.

Was he going to fire her, now that she had been weak and stupid enough to show him that she was still as affected by him as she had been as a senseless teenager? she worried. Or was he determined to hold out for the ultimate prize that would make his vengeance complete—her total capitulation in his bed?

He was rifling through the filing cabinet when she walked into his office and she gritted her teeth, steeling herself for the worst.

'Good morning, Grace.' He pushed the drawer closed without even looking up. 'I trust you slept well?'

Following his impeccably clothed figure with mutinous eyes, she had the strongest desire to hit him as he moved back to his desk.

Restraining the urge, she dragged her wayward appreciation from the silver-grey jacket spanning his broad shoulders to answer bitingly, 'I'd had less than three hours' sleep the previous night. What did you expect?'

He sat down, picked up a gold pen and began writing with it. 'Does that mean you're in better shape to deal with more pressing matters today?'

'What's come up?' She swallowed, despairing at the way her voice faltered. Did this mean that he hadn't summoned her here to fire her?

'The Poulson account. I believe you were dealing with it.' He looked up at her now, and she could have kicked herself from the way the smouldering intensity of his eyes made her stomach flip. 'It seems they're quibbling over assignment dates. It appears from previous correspondence that they can be very difficult to deal with. It also appears that they will only listen to you.'

Grace tried to steady her voice, even though her whole body seemed to be trembling. 'I've built up a rapport with them.' It seemed wrong, talking to him like this, discussing business like formal colleagues, as though those impassioned moments in her flat a little over twelve hours ago had never happened. 'They can be rather awkward at first, but I've found that with a little bit of diplomacy and persuasion they come around.'

From his position of authority his eyes made a cursory survey of her dark-blue slimline skirt, the rather prim little green and navy blouse and her neatly swept-up hair. 'Most people do.'

He applied just the right amount of sexual undertone in the way he said that to bring the colour flooding into her cheeks. There had certainly been nothing diplomatic or persuasive about the way he had urged her into responding to him!

Trying not to look at him, she moved around the desk to pick up the letter he had laid aside for her to look at, at the same time as he reached for his memo pad. His sleeve brushed her bare forearm, a touch so light and yet so sensual that she recoiled from the contact, feeling as though an electrical current was suddenly zinging through her.

Breath held, she urged her feet to carry her over to the filing cabinet, her head swimming. She couldn't concentrate, or even think straight, when he was near her.

'What's wrong, Grace?' He was there, his tanned, very masculine hand rammed flat against the drawer, preventing her from opening it. 'Unwilling to acknowledge what I can still do to you? What we still do to each other?'

Every muscle locking rigid, Grace could scarcely breathe from the alluring, masculine scent of him, from that lethal sexual magnetism that seemed to be pulling her into its dangerous sphere.

'If you're referring to last night, I scarcely knew what I was doing.'

'No?' He looked sceptical.

As well he might! she thought despairingly.

'Why would I want that?' she croaked, clutching the letter she was holding to her breast like it was a lifeline. 'Why, when I despise you? When there aren't words strong enough to describe what you're doing?' A jerk of her head indicated what had been her grandfather's desk and the power it gave the man who sat behind it.

'Because you can't help yourself, Grace, any more than I can.' He was leaning on the cabinet now, his indolent manner unable to conceal that underlying restless vitality about him as he stood supported by his bent arm, one long finger resting against his tough, implacable jaw. 'Oh, don't get me wrong—you aren't my idea of the perfect partner, either. But we aren't talking about a loving, trusting relationship, are we?'

As that finger moved to touch her cheek, Grace twisted her head away in angry rejection.

'I wouldn't have a relationship with you, Seth Mason, if you were the last man left on earth!'

'Such a cliché!' He laughed, a flash of perfect white teeth. 'But I'm not the only man left on earth, am I?' he drawled, that steely gaze dropping to the soft pink bow of her trembling mouth. 'Just the only one you want. And, if that response last night was anything to go by, in as intimate a relationship as it's possible to get.'

As if she needed reminding!

Her throat tight with tension, she flung back at him, 'I had no resistance. I was exhausted—jet-lagged, for heaven's sake!' She brought her chin up to face him squarely, trying to convince him, if not herself, that that was all it had been.

'And have you recovered from your jet lag?'

'Just about. But I…' The pale curve of her forehead puckered, and a guarded look sprang into her cool, clear eyes as she realised where his question was leading. 'Don't you dare,' she warned, backing away from him.

'I told you not to present me with a challenge, Grace,' he reminded her, his arm shooting out as she almost tripped over the waste-paper basket. 'And you seem to make a habit of not looking where you're going.' He laughed softly as that arm snaked around her, but it was the laughter of a victor, of the conqueror claiming his prize.

'Let me go!'

As he swivelled her round, he was still laughing, ignoring the pummelling of her fists against his shoulders as he took her mouth with his in a brutal kiss.

'Why must you always put up a show of fighting me when you know you'll only respond to me eventually?' he mocked softly, lifting his head when her hands gave up trying to make an impression on his hard shoulders. They were now clenched against them in a vain effort not to show him how much they wanted to slide over the smooth cloth spanning his broad back. 'You couldn't help yourself then, last night, and you can't help yourself now, can you?' She couldn't answer. She couldn't say anything, because right at that moment she was too affected by him to speak. 'Perhaps you're one of these women who get their kicks out of being subdued by a man? Is that what it is? Because I'll play that game with you if you want me to—only we'll both know that that's all it is, won't we, Grace? A game.'

Despising herself, Grace wondered how her body could still continue to react to him in the way it did in the light of what was only his need to avenge himself for what she—her family—had done to him in the past. She dragged herself up out of a cauldron of traitorous sensations to toss up at him, 'Go to hell!'

'Oh, I've been there, my love. And I can promise you,

it isn't very pleasant.' His features were chiselled into un-compromising lines. 'But, if making love to me is hell to your pride, then you're going to have to get used to it being scorched raw. Because we're going to burn this thing out between us until there's nothing left but cinders. So don't worry—what we want from each other is so fierce it can't fail to consume itself in the end.'

'And then what?' she asked, shuddering from his determination and the furore of sensations his words were producing in her. 'We both walk away?'

His heavy lids drooped so that she couldn't see the expression in his eyes. 'Naturally.'

Only she wouldn't be able to do that; she was jolted into realizing it. But why? Why, when he meant nothing to her, nothing beyond someone she had had the briefest fling with once? Yet someone whose child she had carried and then lost, as though life had been ridiculing her, exacting payment from her for her naïve and unfeeling indifference.

She closed her eyes against the memories, against the anguish that remembering caused—the longing, the loneliness, the confusion.

'I can't do that.' Involuntarily, the words spilled from her lips; to deflect the meaning he might put on them, she quickly tagged on, 'Contrary to what you might think, I don't go in for casual relationships.'

His lips were but a hair's breadth from hers, so close that even the denial of their consummate touch was a turn on. She brought her eyelids down so that he wouldn't recognise the hunger in her eyes.

'Oh, I think you can.'

Her lashes fluttered apart. His face appeared out of focus, a dark, inscrutable image, mouth hard yet oddly vulnerable, cheeks taut, black lashes drawn down against the wells of his eyes.

He was so incredible. So uncompromisingly handsome. And yet so vengeful.

'Seth, please…' It was uttered from the depths of her longing for the warm and tender lover he had been all those years ago. A tenderness that had been destroyed by the way both she and her family had treated him. 'Don't do this.'

He moved back a little so that he could see her more clearly. 'Begging, Grace?'

That cruel curve to his mouth showed her, with deepening despair, that there was going to be no reprieve for her.

'No, just trying to appeal to your better nature, but that's obviously a waste of time!'

'Obviously.' He smiled, an action still devoid of any warmth. 'How can you expect restraint from someone who's… what was it you called me?…basic? Now, let me see: what does that mean? Rough? Primitive? Lacking in social graces? Well, don't worry. I'm sure I can knock all your ex-public-school lovers into a cocked hat! When I make love to you there's going to be none of the haste or urgency that we were driven by the first time. You're going to have all the benefit of my cultivated experience in a long slow night of love play befitting a woman of your…sophistication. And you're not going to get out of that bed until you're so drunk on sex with me you'll be unable to stand. Is that clear?'

The hot retort that sprang to Grace's lips was stalled by a sudden knock on the door.

Pulling out of his orbit, she was still tugging her blouse straight when Simone came in carrying some files.

'You wanted these, Mr Mason.'

Distractedly, Grace noticed her PA's eyes dart from her to Seth and then back to her again; she noticed, too, the crisp white handkerchief stained with her lipstick that Seth was pocketing as he turned round, calmly, coolly, as though the air wasn't charged with a sexual tension so thick that it left

Grace trembling, and which she knew the other woman must surely be able to feel.

'Yes, thanks, Simone. Did you bring your note pad as well?'

He had known her PA was coming up here, Grace thought, aghast, as the other woman laughed a little nervously at something else he said before sitting down. Yet he had still tried to seduce her again in spite of that? What had been his intention? she wondered, fuming—to hope that Simone was the type of tactless employee who thrived on office scandal and would let everyone in the office know that they were having an affair?

His upward glance at Grace from where he was sitting now was almost one of surprise to still see her there.

'Thank you, Grace, he said, his tone crisp, cold, formal. 'That will be all.'

He had the audacity to dismiss her, like she was some temp he could call up or dismiss whenever the fancy took him! Or, worse, some fawning little sex-slave at his beck and call.

Well, if he wanted office gossip, she decided, grabbing the letter off the top of the cabinet she realised he'd taken from her, then she'd let him have it.

'Don't keep him too long,' she uttered, bending, piqued, towards Simone. 'He's got a heavy appointment coming up this afternoon. Nasty maintenance case.' Voice lowered, she wrinkled her nose in a knowing little gesture. 'Best keep it under your hat.'

From Simone's obvious discomfort, the woman was clearly unsure whether Grace was joking or not. Although Grace knew that her PA would keep any personal information about her employers to herself, Seth didn't know that.

She didn't even bother looking at him again before sweeping out of the office, a tight little set to her mouth, her head held high.

* * *

The next couple of weeks passed in a hectic blur of board meetings, legal work and negotiations, then Seth was away for a few days, engaged in aspects of his diverse business-interests elsewhere.

There had been too much to do in the office for other, more personal distractions, and when Seth was called away unexpectedly to sort out yet another problem in his business empire that couldn't be delegated, Grace couldn't have been more relieved.

Just like everyone else, she had worked hard over that initial period to get the transition of management running smoothly, staying late at the office, sometimes going without meals—something she had often done in the past, much to her grandfather's disapproval. But Seth was a phenomenon with reserves of energy that outstripped hers and even the most dynamic of the other executives and she was determined, if she could, to try to keep up with him. How he managed to control his business interests, keeping them all running efficiently even from a span of hundreds of miles, was beyond Grace—although it did give credit to his judgement in engaging only the best staff needed to run each and every enterprise he presided over.

Which made his decision to have her working closely with him something she might have taken a pride in, if it hadn't been for the knowledge that he harboured a bitter desire to make her pay for her actions in the past—and in the most basic way possible. So whenever he was around, his presence alone seemed to shatter her equilibrium, stretching her nerves as taut as guitar strings, so that she began losing sleep as well.

'You look ghastly,' he remarked when he returned briefly late one afternoon on a flying visit to the office. 'Simone tells me you've been working all hours and neglecting to look after yourself—like missing lunch on more occasions than is healthy—and we can't have that, can we? I don't want a weak, undernourished lover in my bed.'

'Then you'll just have to find yourself one with more generous proportions, won't you?' Grace threw back, refraining from telling him that she'd had a recent stomach upset, which was probably why she looked so pale. She was unwilling to acknowledge how fit, strong and how terrifyingly attractive he looked in comparison, with the brilliant white collar of his shirt emphasising his olive skin and his black, untameable hair and that fine-tailored dark suit he was wearing accentuating the lean, hard lines of his body. 'I'm sure you'll find plenty at Weight Watchers!'

He laughed, as he always did when she tried to fend off his determined remarks about making her his mistress.

'You'll eat,' he ordered, catching her hand. 'Starting now.' A glance at the clock on the wall showed that it was already four-thirty.

'Not with you.' She tried to pull away but his grip only tightened in response.

'With me. And on my expense account. This is a business dinner, and one I expect you to honour.'

He meant it; she could always tell when business came uppermost on his agenda. Which was how, twenty minutes later, she found herself being handed out of the chauffeur-driven Mercedes he often used around the city and guided into the tastefully furnished little restaurant which was glowing with seasonal warmth and which, Seth had told her on hte way there, served exquisitely cooked meals throughout the day.

'I hadn't realised how hungry I was,' she accepted reluctantly as she tucked into a home-made lasagne with salad and huge chunks of crusty bread, while Seth had a gammon steak with all the trimmings.

'I thought you might want to see this,' he said when they had finished.

It was an email addressed to Seth, from the customers that Grace had visited in New York, agreeing to continue to trade with Culverwells now that it was under Mason's corporate umbrella.

'That must make you feel quite smug,' she remarked, unable to keep the edge out of her voice.

'Not at all.' He wiped his mouth with his napkin, laid it down on the table. 'The PR job you did in New York obviously paid off.' So he was acknowledging now that she hadn't flown off to the Big Apple just to go designer shopping, as he'd originally accused her of doing. 'And *I'm* in this simply to restore Culverwells to a healthy balance sheet.'

'And to make yourself even more millions while doing so.'

'Well, naturally. I'm a businessman,' he stressed, pushing his empty plate forward before sitting back on his chair. 'That would obviously come into the equation. But one thing I'm not in this business for is to antagonise you.'

'Really?' She looked at him dubiously, picking up her glass of sparkling water, which reflected the festive, coloured lights adorning the bar. 'You could have fooled me.'

'That's a totally separate issue,' he stated, ignoring the jibe. 'One thing I learned on the road to where I am now is never to let personal and business dealings overlap. Did you know your grandfather took risks in other areas that weren't always to the good of the company?'

His question, coming out of the blue, threw her for a moment. She looked at him over her glass, a mixture of puzzlement and wounded accusation in her eyes.

'My grandfather would never have done anything underhanded.'

'I'm not saying he did.' He had ordered one small glass of wine for himself—rich and ruby red—which left tears around the bowl as he finished drinking, and put the glass back down on the oak-stained table. 'He invested unwisely—with the best intentions, I'm sure, but against the advice of more circumspect members of his board. By then his judgement was probably clouded by more…personal matters.' Which, as he had already pointed out, he himself would never allow to happen. 'Ones that, I believe he realised at the end, hadn't really been worth risking his company for.'

He meant Corinne, but Grace wasn't sure what else he was driving at.

'What do you mean?' she queried, her forehead pleating.

'Did you know that your grandfather had made an appointment with his solicitor for the day after he died with the intention of changing his will?' Grace felt the colour drain from her face. 'You didn't.' Amazingly, that strong-boned face was etched with something almost close to commiseration.

She shook her head several times as though to clear it. 'How did you find out?'

'I have my sources.'

Of course. He would have access to everything now—letters. Files. Company diaries. Even her, if she allowed herself to succumb to that lethal attraction.

'Perhaps he realised the mistake he was making and had decided to do something about it,' he said.

But instead he had had that heart attack, and his real wishes had never been known. She wondered if Seth was thinking what she was—that if Lance Culverwell hadn't died when he had things could have been so different. Grace would probably have control of the company, and Seth could never have taken it over as he had.

'I'm afraid all your admirable efforts to save Culverwells wouldn't have amounted to anything without the injection of cash it sorely needed for reinvestment,' she heard Seth telling her, as if he knew the path her thoughts had taken.

Which only a man with his obvious wealth and influence could provide, she acknowledged reluctantly.

'Be careful,' she murmured. She was choked by her feelings for the grandfather she'd been unable to help believing had let her down, on top of a barrage of conflicting emotions towards the man sitting opposite her—although for reasons she didn't dare to question. 'That sounded suspiciously like a compliment.'

'Your ability as a businesswoman, Grace, has never been in any doubt.'

She made a sceptical sound down her nostrils. 'But other aspects of my character have?' When an elevated eyebrow was his only response, she went on, 'Anyway, that isn't what you said the day you took over Culverwells.'

'I know what I said,' he rasped. 'That was before I'd had a chance to study just how hard you've worked and how much you've put into the firm, given of yourself, to get the best out of your fellow directors and your staff.' He lifted his glass again. 'I salute you, Grace. It isn't every day, in my experience, one comes across such single-minded dedication—particularly in a woman. And before you say I'm being sexist—' he put up his other hand, staving off the retort that was teetering on her lips '—I'm not. I merely stated in my *own* experience. Most of the women I've known in top management have had to split their time between their jobs and their families, particularly their children, which makes it very hard to remain ruthlessly single-minded indefinitely. You, fortunately, have had no such distractions.'

'No.' With a rueful curl to her mouth she looked down at her glass, wondering what he would have said had he known that if fate hadn't intervened she would have had a child now. And not just any child. *His* child.

'Come on,' he said, surprisingly gently, perhaps sensing her sudden change of mood, probably thinking it was because of losing her previous position in the company. 'I'll take you home.'

The gallery lights below her flat had only just gone out when the huge white car pulled up outside.

'Beth's been working late,' Grace commented, getting out

of the car just as the gallery door opened and the curvy little brunette came out.

Exchanging a few words with her friend, Grace couldn't help noticing the way Beth looked appreciatively at Seth who was moving around the bonnet of the gleaming white Mercedes.

'How do you do it?' she whispered to Grace, clearly awe-struck.

Reluctantly, because Seth had overheard, Grace introduced Beth to him. What woman was safe from him? she despaired as the two of them shook hands and the gallery manager seemed to visibly melt beneath Seth's devastating smile.

'So, you're the Seth Mason I've been hearing all about!' All smiles herself, Beth sounded slightly breathless as she let Seth know with that unusually tactless remark that Grace had been discussing him with her. 'Didn't I see you at the opening night?' She looked at Grace then back to the tall, rather untamed-looking man beside her for confirmation.

'It's…possible,' Seth answered rather evasively.

'It's all right, Beth, I'll lock up,' Grace offered, relieved when her friend took the hint and tripped lightly away without causing Grace any further embarrassment, after falling over herself to express her pleasure at having met Seth.

'Going to ask me in for coffee?'

He was standing there just behind her and, after he had just bought her the meal, Grace didn't feel she could refuse.

When she complied somewhat uneasily, she saw him nod briefly to his driver.

'You said coffee—not breakfast,' she reminded him with her heart racing as the large saloon pulled away.

'He was parked on double yellows. He'll amuse himself without breaking any traffic regulations until I give him a call.'

Which told *her*, she thought, feeling suitably chastened. She was relieved though that the gallery door was still unlocked, which meant that she could take him through to the small sitting room at the back of the shop rather than up to the crowding intimacy of her flat.

Flicking on the lights and securing the doors behind him so that no one would think the gallery was still open, she left him browsing the display of paintings while she went through to the tiny kitchen behind the stock room and made two mugs of instant coffee, pouring milk into her own and remembering that, in the office, Seth always drank his black.

He was studying a simply framed pen-and-ink seascape which was concealed from public view in a small recess behind the counter when she came back. He stooped closer, reading the scrawled signature at the bottom.

'Matthew Tyler.'

'My father.'

He took the mug she handed to him. 'Of course. I understand his paintings sell for thousands—tens of thousands—these days.'

Grace nodded.

'I believe his sculptures aren't doing so badly, either.' When she didn't respond with so much as a gesture this time, he tagged on, 'You must be very proud of him.'

Was she?

To avoid answering, she took a hasty sip of her coffee and burnt her tongue in the process.

'I didn't really know him,' she said, trying to sound non-committal when she had recovered enough to speak.

'And is this the only thing you have of his?' He glanced at her briefly.

'Besides this shop?'

She was reminded from his lack of surprise that he knew about that already. 'No loft full of unsold masterpieces?'

'I should be so lucky,' she said with a grimace. 'I don't think he'd done anything for a long time before he died. Anything that wasn't unfinished or crossed through had been sold, or thrown away. I've been told he was an obsessive perfectionist.'

'So this was all he left you to remember him by?' He was still studying the sketch, his Adam's apple working as he took sips of his coffee.

'Well, no, to be fair, there was one other item.'

He sliced her a glance, obviously expecting her to enlarge, but she didn't.

With her head tilted to one side, she gave her attention to the drawing. 'It's good,' she appraised a little stiffly. 'But it isn't one of his best.'

His best, according to the experts, was the bronze figure she had sold, created from a sketch that Matthew Tyler had made of his daughter during one of his rare and fleeting appearances in her life. He had only come to see her then, during those agonising weeks after her miscarriage, because Lance Culverwell had sent for him, because she had been so unwell, so low...

'The sculptures were his forte,' she told him with her gaze still trained on the wall, wondering if those intelligent eyes she could feel suddenly resting on her profile could guess at the tension behind her tightly controlled features.

How could she talk about that bronze to anyone—least of all him? Explain the emotions that had driven her to selling it?

She didn't even chance looking at Seth, afraid that he would see those emotions now scoring her face.

'What is it?' he asked quietly, far, far too aware.

She gave a gasp as the lights in the gallery suddenly went out, leaving them in darkness.

'Oh, no, not a power cut,' Grace groaned, though she was grateful for the diversion from his probing question in spite of the inconvenience of having no electricity.

'I...don't think so.' Seth was looking at the festively lit shops on the other side of the road and the street lamp that was glowing brightly immediately outside the gallery. 'It might be that something's blown your fuses,' he stated.

She uttered a nervous little laugh. 'Just my luck!'

'Do you know where your trip switch is?'

When she told him he went through without any hesitation to fix the problem. A couple of seconds later, the lights came on, but then instantly went out again.

'Do you have any other appliances switched on?' he queried.

'Only the fridge.'

'Anything upstairs?'

'Again, the fridge…'

'What is it?' he asked, seeing her frown.

'I put the dishwasher on before I left this morning. But that would have finished hours ago.'

'I think you'd better let me check.'

As soon as she opened the door of the flat to let them in, she could feel the heat coming from the kitchen.

Seth shot her an urgent glance. 'What time did you say you put it on?'

Grace looked at him anxiously. 'Before I left for work…'

Three strides brought him across her tiny kitchen. He cancelled the switch on the wall above the worktop before opening the door of the overheated appliance, stepping quickly aside as a cloud of steam gushed out.

'I don't think there's any doubt that your dishes are clean,' he remarked dryly. He was down on his haunches now, pulling the lower basket towards him, and Grace felt her gaze drawn to the way the dark-grey fabric of his trousers strained across his thighs as he inspected the shiny interior of her dishwasher for any obvious damage.

'It's been going all this time?' It was an amazed little utterance, dragged from a throat suddenly dry from a riveting sexual awareness.

'Seems like the programmer's stuck,' he diagnosed authoritatively. He was pushing the basket back in, but stopped in mid-action. 'Hardly a load worth putting on, was it?' he commented, noting the sparsity of dishes in both baskets.

Grace made a small gesture with her shoulders. 'Believe it or not, I don't spend all my time in this flat cooking.'

'Obviously not.' His speculative smile left little doubt as to what he thought she spent most of her time doing. Probably entertaining a steady stream of boyfriends! she thought hopelessly. 'But that doesn't alter the fact that you're not eating enough.' His eyes, skimming over her willowy figure beneath her black executive suit, admonished as much as they admired. 'Worrying about something, Grace?' The sound of the dishwasher door clicking closed only added to an air of menace Grace could almost touch as he got to his feet, so that she was far too affected by him to answer. 'We're going to have to do something about that, aren't we?' he said.

Aware of the worktop against the small of her back, Grace swallowed, feeling absurdly trapped. The way he was looking at her with that smouldering regard—as though he knew that the reason she couldn't eat or sleep properly was because she was so wound up over him—left her in no doubt, after that last remark, as to what he was going to do about it.

One of the sleeves of his suit was pushed up, exposing a good deal of immaculate white cuff. Those loose strands of hair that fell tantalisingly over his forehead even though he'd raked them back were curling damply from the steam. He looked flushed, dishevelled and incredibly sexy.

'Come here, Grace,' he urged softly.

CHAPTER SIX

SHE didn't want to. She wanted to ask him to leave. But his eyes were as compelling as his voice had been and, while her lips wouldn't move, her feet had no such reservations.

Fuelled by an inner fire that his masculinity had stoked, as much a slave to her desire for him now as that teenager had been all those years ago, she moved towards him, drawn by an insistence stronger than her will, stronger even than all her instincts of self-survival.

When she was but half a pace away he reached out and let his fingers curl around the nape of her neck, closing those extra inches as he brought his head down to hers.

Surprisingly, his lips grazed one corner of her mouth, so gently that Grace sucked in her breath from the exquisite tenderness of his action.

His breath was warm and so feather-light against the curve of her cheek that the sensuality of it sent shivers along her spine. She turned her head, her mouth aching for contact with his. He laughed softly, denying it, drawing a small, plaintive sound from her lips.

'Why rush it?' he whispered against her ear, and even the deep timbre of his voice was arousing her—as he knew it would, she realised helplessly, lured deeper into the sensual heaven he was creating for her.

With one hand resting against his shirt beneath his open

jacket, Grace could feel the warmth of him and the steady rhythm of his heart. His biceps flexed under fingers that were locked tensely onto his immaculate sleeve just below his shoulder. Even the cut and elegance of his clothes couldn't disguise his latent strength, the whipcord power of his body.

'Seth…' she murmured as wanting became a need that spread like bushfire, radiating excitement, heat and tension along her veins.

'Pleading?' he mocked softly. But then he was covering her mouth with his own, his arms coming fully around her, pulling her into the hard angles of his taut, aroused body, his groan lost in the warm cavern that was yielding to his sensual plunder now.

No man had ever made her feel like this, Grace acknowledged, her arms sliding up around his neck. No one! *Only this man!* And now she knew why all her potential relationships with other men had failed. Because after Seth she had wanted to feel like this with someone else, just once, and it had never happened for her. Never in eight long years.

The scent of him was intoxicating as her eager fingers slid into the dark strength of his hair, locking him to her to prolong the kiss, wanting it never to stop.

When he did it was only to allow his lips to follow the scented column of her throat, forcing her head back as her body reacted with a will of its own, arching, yielding, guiding him along its secret paths to unleash the pleasure to which only he had ever possessed the key.

Somehow he had tugged open her blouse and pushed aside the scalloped lace of her white bra, and as his mouth closed over the erect, tingling peak of her breast the pleasure spilled out in a spiral of throbbing need.

'Seth…'

She shouldn't be doing this! There was a frantic little voice inside her head: *he despises you!* she tried telling herself. But her feeble attempts to remind herself were lost in the delirious heat of all that he was doing to her as she helped him remove her jacket and blouse, and felt him release the button on her skirt and draw down the zip like it was second nature to him to be undressing her.

He murmured some appreciative sound as the clinging little garment slid to the floor, followed by the bra he had unclasped, so that she was standing there in only her white satin string and sheer black hold-ups.

Later she would regret this, she knew, but for now what did it matter what he thought about her? All that mattered was that she was in his arms, this man who had been born to be her lover, because he was right, she accepted with a painful intensity. He was the only man she wanted. The only man she had ever wanted.

His hands caressed her breasts, his slightly callused palms an excruciating pleasure as they teased and tormented the pale, swollen aureoles.

Wild for him, drugged with desire, she tugged at the buttons of his shirt, allowing him to help her in removing his jacket, dragging his shirt out of his waistband.

The feel of his taut, warm skin as he pulled her back against his hair-roughened body sent pulsing sensations rocketing through her.

Her breathing laboured, Grace caught his groan of need, her excitement a stifling heat that held her rigid as he moved to allow his tongue to travel down and down along her eager body.

He was on his knees, his long fingers caressing the gentle curve of her buttocks, playing across the smooth, pale flesh above the black lacy tops of her stockings.

She moved convulsively and he caught her to him, his mouth hot against the core of her femininity beneath the damp scented satin of her string.

She was on that beach again, paralysed by the depth of her

wanting, her body moving of its own accord, for him to douse the fire he had aroused in the only way it could be doused.

'Oh, mercy…' He shuddered violently against her and the next instant he was lifting her up, finding his way instinctively to the room with the big double bed.

Somehow they were lying there naked together and those hands caressing her body were as familiar as a pathway home.

She jerked against him, eager for his possession, but he was determined to make her wait, treating her to a practised and abandoned eternity of consummate love-play, just as he had promised he would.

A long time later when she was damp and sobbing with desire, thinking she would die of wanting if he didn't take her soon, gently he parted her thighs and with one rapturous thrust slid into the slick, wet warmth of her body, blowing her mind with his slow, calculated control.

With a driving need, she curled her fingers along the velvet-sheathed strength of his back, her body closing around his, writhing beneath him like a mad thing until the swift, sharp crescendo of orgasm that made her cry out. It seemed to go on and on, until the thrusts that were driving her became harder and more urgent, and the fluid warmth of him erupted and flowed into her, finally dousing the mutual fire of their passion.

Some time afterwards he raised himself up and looked at her. Her hair lay like a silver cloud over the pillow. Her face was flushed and damp from the ecstasy they had shared. Her eyelashes, though, were drawn down, as though she didn't want to look at him—or couldn't.

Marvelling at how beautiful she was, a warm pleasure curved his mouth from the way she had made him feel, as though he were the only man on earth—or, amazingly, the only one that mattered—and on a breath that seemed to shudder through him, he murmured, 'Look at me, Grace.'

The eyes she raised reluctantly to his were dark and slumberous from the aftermath of their love-making, but as they tugged over his face something clouded their depths and in a barbed tone she said, 'Why? So you can claim yet another victory for yourself?'

Her unexpected response surprisingly cut him like a whiplash.

Of course. She hadn't been able to help herself, any more than he had. They were bound to wind up in bed together whether they liked each other or not. And it was clearly "or not" in her case, he realised, mocking that moment's conceit when he had imagined otherwise.

So what had he been expecting? he challenged himself roughly. Declarations of undying love from her? His inward laughter was mirthless and cold. Of course not. He wouldn't have welcomed that from her in any case. Or would he? The thought struck him suddenly. He had to admit that it would be a rather ironic turn up for the books.

'If that's the way you want to view it.' Self-ridicule put a chill in his voice now. 'Although for one supposedly beaten you sounded pretty triumphant at the end.'

Shame scorched Grace's cheeks. How could she have let it happen? she remonstrated with herself, mortified that he had seen her so helpless and begging. But that was exactly what this whole seduction thing had been about, she realised hopelessly, wanting to bury her head under the pillow and never come up for air.

'I take it there's no chance of your getting pregnant?' Seth's question was curt, matter-of-fact.

Coldly reminded of all she had been through after the way she had behaved with him the first time, Grace pressed her eyelids closed, immensely relieved that at least she was protected by the Pill she had started taking shortly before her cancelled wedding.

Nevertheless, she couldn't help biting out, 'Isn't it a bit late to ask me that now?'

It was, and he could have kicked himself for not giving it too much consideration beforehand, but then she had blown his mind with her abandoned response.

'Well?' It was a hard, emotionless demand.

'Don't worry.' Rolling away from him, Grace leapt to her feet and self-consciously scrambled around for the robe that she'd left draped across the bottom of her bed that morning. 'I won't be coming after you with a paternity suit,' she assured him caustically, finding the robe in a pool of pale satin on the carpet. 'If that's what you're worrying about.'

'Do I take it then that you're on the Pill?'

Propped up on an elbow, he reclined there, watching her, totally unfazed by the fact that he was naked while she was struggling to bring both ends of her robe together, ridiculously embarrassed after what they had just done.

'Take it any way you like!' Finding it almost impossible to keep her eyes from those heavily muscled limbs and hard, lean torso, when he had just used that devastating masculinity of his to subdue her, she swung away from him towards the bathroom, not anticipating the speed at which he could come after her until he was pulling her round to face him before she was even halfway towards the door.

'What are you trying to do?' His fingers bit into her arm. 'Deny that it happened?'

How could she? She still wanted to slide her hands over his magnificent body, surrender to its warm strength and thrusting power with a pleasure unequalled by anything else in the universe.

'No,' she uttered shakily, looking past him so she wouldn't have to focus on the harsh sweep of his jaw and that hard, incisive mouth that had made her cry out with the screaming intimacy of its kisses. The musky scent of him that was filling her nostrils was a taunting reminder of how uninhibitedly their juices had fused. 'Just trying to come to terms with being such a fool.'

'Don't let it get you down.' He released her with almost careless indifference. 'The feeling does wear off eventually.' And on that scathing note he turned away, leaving her fleeing to the bathroom with the stinging reminder of how she had once made an equal fool of him.

Fortunately, Seth flew off the following morning to pursue some new accounts in the States, which gave Grace time to recover her composure and a little bit of dignity. She didn't know how she would have faced him, particularly in front of the rest of the board, Simone and other members of staff, knowing that she had played right into his hands and handed him on a plate the conquest he had been planning.

As she took telephone calls, attended meetings and made appointments for the week ahead, she kept asking herself—as she had been doing constantly since before she had come out of her bathroom the previous night and found that Seth had already left—why she had let things get so out of hand between them.

He had shown her a soft side of himself yesterday that had lured her into a false sense of security, and like a prize idiot she had fallen for it when she knew how much he despised her and how little respect he had for her. Consequently, she only had herself to blame.

She groaned at her senseless behaviour, so unable to think of anything else that she cut off a caller who wanted to speak to the marketing manager and got through the rest of her work like an automaton. Her only consolation, she thought, racked by shame and self-reproach, was that she'd learned her lesson the first time and that at least this time there wouldn't be any repercussions from their love-making.

Seth didn't return at all that week. Having already put things in place to keep the company running smoothly while he was away, he telephoned some time during the following week to say that he expected to be out of the country for the rest of the month.

He didn't speak to Grace personally, however, leaving the message with Simone. Hurting and angry, Grace decided that, having achieved everything he had set out to do—taking control of Culverwells, then securing her ultimate humiliation by taking her to bed—he was obviously now treating her with the contempt he thought she deserved.

Christmas came and went with still no word from him, and her wretchedness was only compounded by a heavy cold.

Having spent the holiday alone, being forced to miss a party at Beth's, and with Corinne having flown off to Madeira on Christmas Eve, Grace returned to work on a wet January morning feeling as though she was the only person in London that Christmas had done a detour round, and with the knowledge that Seth wasn't due to return for another week.

And, if that wasn't enough to deal with, her period was overdue.

At first she put it down simply to stress. Stress could be responsible for a lot of things and over the past couple of months she had had a lot of things to be stressed about.

No way could she be pregnant, she assured herself resolutely. Fate couldn't do that to her twice.

But, beneath her over-confident attempts to dismiss any possibility that she might be, lay the nagging truth that she was worried sick. She'd been protected, when she and Seth had made love, it was true, but she was only on a low-dosage Pill, and she had had a stomach upset a couple of days before. She hadn't even thought of it at the time, but of course something like that could render the Pill ineffective. It didn't help reminding herself that her periods were as regular as clockwork. That there was only one other time in her life that her period had ever been late…

Around mid-week, feeling queasy and off-colour, she

decided to buy a pregnancy test. And it was then, in the lonely privacy of her flat, where she had behaved so foolishly with the man whose only plan was to make her pay, that her worst fears were realised.

She was having Seth Mason's child—again!

'You OK?' Simone glanced up at her young boss with matronly concern as Grace emerged from the 'ladies' just outside her PA's office. She had darted in there a few minutes before, overcome by a bout of sickness.

'I'm fine, Simone.' Grace wanted to dismiss any suggestion that she wasn't, unwilling to draw attention to herself or her pregnancy. But she had just seen herself in the ladies' room mirror and had been shocked by how washed out she looked, with her black pin-striped suit emphasising the sickly pallor of her skin.

'Yeah?' Simone sounded as sceptical as she looked. 'And my name's Errrol Flynn and I swing from chandeliers for a living.'

Grace couldn't help but smile wanly at the images that conjured up. 'I'd like to see that,' she murmured, too under par even to want to talk right then. 'Honestly, Simone, I'm fine.' She managed to inject just the right degree of authority in her voice to silence her concerned PA; she was glad of her standing in the company which gave her the right to pull rank, that she seldom exercised, so that she could escape to the privacy of her own office.

The phone was ringing on her desk before she even had chance to sit down.

'How are you getting on with that hunk you're answerable to now?' Corinne enquired from her yacht somewhere in the tepid waters of Madeira, sounding far too breezy. 'And don't tell me you're not enjoying it, because he's the type of man that could satisfy even someone with as many sexual hang-ups as you.'

Sighing, Grace rued the day that she had confided in her grandfather's young wife about her lack of desire for the men she dated; she'd been especially worried when her real lack of enthusiasm had extended even to Paul.

'Did you know my grandfather knew of Seth Mason from years ago?' she asked the model, not feeling up to having this conversation with her. 'And that he would have done anything to keep him from pushing his way into his company's boardroom?'

'Not pushing, Grace, dear—storming it. And with all that lovely drive and crackling authority!' That the woman was smitten by Seth's looks and dangerous charm was obvious to Grace. 'Anyway, what do you mean?' She could almost see the redhead's green eyes narrowing in anticipation of some juicy snippet of information about him, and realised too late that she had said too much when Corinne, her voice dropping confidentially, enquired, 'What did he do? Try to have his wicked way with you?'

She laughed, supposedly at the improbability of it. But it was so on the mark that Grace couldn't contain the sharp little breath that escaped her. 'Good heavens! Is that it?' Corinne was far too shrewd not to have noticed. 'My word! Have I hit the nail on the head? Is that why you're so opposed to working for him? What did he do, Grace, spoil you for every other man?' Corinne's amused tones were just a little too loud, far too triumphant. 'You aren't frigid, love. You were just weaned on the wrong type of man far too soon.'

The wrong type of man full-stop! Grace thought, hating him, angry with him and with herself—for wanting him, for missing him like crazy, and for allowing herself to get pregnant—twice!—by the man she had once snubbed. Only now he was snubbing her, and it wasn't very nice. No, worse than that—it hurt like hell!

But why? she asked herself, agonised. She wasn't in love with him, was she? Or had she just been kidding herself all along? Was that why she had never been able to indulge in casual sexual relationships with men as some of her contemporaries did? Or even find the degree of pleasure she should have found with the man she had been planning to marry? Was it because she had found her soulmate in a man her upbringing had forced her to reject? The man with whom she had compared all other men she met, only to find them lacking in every way?

'Stop dreaming up romantic dramas, Corinne,' she parried, shaken by the possibility, and desperate to keep the ex-model from realising that she had guessed the truth—or at least part of it, at any rate. No way was she ready to accept that all her problems with men stemmed from a void in her life that only Seth Mason could fill.

'Granddad would have been appalled by what you did. Culverwells is going to wind up being sold off. Seth says he won't do that, but I don't believe it.' And in a sudden rush of anger, because she hadn't seen him, because she didn't know where he was and because she had been unfortunate enough to conceive his child when he didn't even like her, she blurted out, 'He's a money-making, social-climbing, mercenary opportunist! And if you ever see him again, you can tell him I said so!'

'Why don't you tell him yourself?' Corinne's voice suddenly sounded sultry, oddly provocative. 'He's sitting right here on deck beside me. It's Grace. I think she's missing you.' There was no attempt on Corinne's part to cover the mouthpiece.

In a mortified daze, Grace grabbed the edge of her desk for support. Seth was on her grandfather's yacht? Seth was in Madeira with Corinne?

'Hello, Grace.' As it started to sink in that he must have heard everything that her grandfather's widow had been saying about her, that deep voice coming down the line was agonising torment. 'Is everything all right?'

No, it blasted well isn't!

Then, as it dawned that Corinne must know everything that had been going on between Seth and herself, in a voice raw with accusation she exhaled, 'Did you tell her?'

'Tell her?' He sounded puzzled. 'Tell her what?'

'About us?' She imagined them together, discussing her, laughing about it.

'What is there to tell?'

'For goodness' sake! Do I have to spell it out?' He was stalling for time, making her sweat—and enjoying every minute of it. 'You know exactly what I'm talking about.'

'Now, come on, Grace. You know what I said about kissing and telling.'

'Oh, thanks a bundle!' Now Corinne wouldn't be in any doubt about what had gone on between them. 'So now you've made sure she knows, if she didn't before!' The pain she felt inside was excruciating, but she forced herself to continue even as she collapsed, sick with herself, onto her chair. 'I suppose you're getting immense satisfaction out of this?'

'No more than you were when you tried to convince Simone—and probably the whole office—that I was involved in a paternity suit.'

His words made her flinch. Well the joke had backfired on her. And how!

'So that's what this is—tit for tat? Let the spoilt, stuck-up little brat stew while you're sunning yourself with Corinne and having a good laugh over it at my expense? Why not just shout it to the crew? Why not tell everybody what we did? You're worse than unscrupulous, you're…!'

'Hold your horses, Grace. Corinne's gone below.'

'What for?' she enquired pointedly. 'Her bikini top?'

'You think I'm bedding your grandfather's widow?'

'Is that what they call it, lying bare-breasted on the open deck of a yacht? Or has she gone down to warm up that nice, big double bed for you?'

'What's really eating you, Grace?' He was beginning to sound annoyed. 'Are you jealous?'

'Hah! Don't be ridiculous!' she retorted, feeling a wave of nausea wash over her. She took a deep breath to try and stave off the feeling before she went on. 'It may surprise you to know that I don't care what you do. Just don't do it in my company's time!'

'It isn't your company—it's mine.' All levity had gone from his voice. 'And so help me, Grace, if I was in the building right now I'd come straight down to your office and take you over my knee.'

The anger trickling down the line from goodness knew how many miles away was a tangible thing in the silence that followed.

Through an imprisoning sexual tension, Grace could hear the water lapping against the side of the boat, hear the wind tugging at the rigging, a mixture of sounds confused and distorted by the ringing of a phone somewhere in another office and the deep, rhythmic sound of the photocopier on Simone's desk.

'I'm here to finalise a deal,' he stressed before she could recover her vexed and wounded pride enough to deal with that last sexist remark. 'But I'll be back in the office next week, and then I'll give both you and the company all the attention you need. Now, what was it you wanted?'

'Wanted?'

'Why did you ring me? Is there some problem?'

Trying to clear her head, Grace only then remembered that Corinne had telephoned *her*, whether to make her jealous, or in some weird, sadistic way to see how she would cope having her private emotions discussed in front of Seth, she wasn't sure.

'Yes,' she breathed, so humiliated now that she didn't care if she did ruin his week, wanting to make things as difficult and as painful for him as he was making them for her in being with Corinne. That was impossible, though, she thought, because nothing could hurt him as much as she was hurting as she spat out bitterly, 'I'm pregnant!'

CHAPTER SEVEN

THE phone she slammed down started ringing almost immediately, and even without checking the number on the display Grace knew it would be Seth.

When she didn't pick it up, it continued to ring, a shrill insistence that cut through her tension, causing the embryo of a pain to start throbbing on either side of her temples. At last the ringing stopped.

Good; let him stew! she thought, gritting her teeth against her headache and her suffocating misery. But instantly the phone started ringing again.

When she didn't respond this time, the merciful seconds' silence that followed was immediately broken by her mobile phone ringing in her bag on the shelf behind her desk.

Grabbing the bag, she found the phone with fingers that shook, and with more than a degree of unusual force switched it off.

She couldn't—wouldn't—give him the satisfaction of venting his frustrations on her now. If she was going to have to suffer all over again for her stupidity in going to bed with him, then he was going to as well, she agonised with bitter tears stinging her eyes just as a call came through on her internal line.

'What is it?' She knew the answer even before she heard the receptionist's harassed response.

'It's Mr Mason. He's on line one. He's having difficulty getting through to your office.'

'Tell Mr Mason I'm not taking any calls.'

There was a brief hesitation. 'I can't do that.' Grace could almost feel the girl's horror at even being asked to contemplate contradicting their new chief executive.

'Then tell him I'm out,' Grace instructed, her mouth tightening at the sway Seth held over what had been her grandfather's and then her staff.

'I can't do that either.' The disembodied voice sounded even more diffident. 'He already knows you aren't.'

Feeling sorry for the girl and not wanting to put her in an awkward position, Grace grabbed her coat and, imparting a resolute, 'Well, I am now!' she made a hurried exit from the building.

It was wet and murky outside and cold needles of rain stung her face, as she'd left her umbrella in the office. The bare trees around the square she turned into looked like dark shadows of their former selves, and even the houses and shops looked dreary and left-over now that the festive season was gone.

She needed to get out, she told herself in an attempt to justify dropping everything and making her escape from the office, a thing which under normal circumstances she would never even have considered. But these weren't normal circumstances, were they?

The fact of her pregnancy had still scarcely sunk in when Corinne's call had come through, and the woman had made those very personal remarks about her—in front of Seth. Only Grace hadn't known that Seth was with Corinne up until that point. Until then she had simply been wondering how she was going to tell him about her pregnancy.

Anger and jealousy tore at her as she thought about him with Corinne; imagined them lying on the sun deck of that yacht, limbs entwined, pale skin yielding to the sinewy strength of dark bronze.

What would it matter to him that she was carrying his child? She was a woman of the world—or so he thought. Women of the world could handle little set-backs in their lives like unwanted pregnancies, particularly if they weren't in love with the child's father. And she wasn't in love with him, was she? she asked herself fiercely. How could she be with a man who could treat her so badly? Who was determined to make her pay for the way she had treated him when she'd been a spoilt teenager, no matter what the cost?

The blast of a van's horn brought her up sharply as she made to cross the busy road, and she jumped back onto the pavement, berating herself for jeopardising not only her own life but her unborn baby's too.

She wasn't a woman of the world. She would have this baby and she would bear the consequences, she determined grittily. It was just that it was going to be so humiliating, facing Seth.

She hadn't planned to shout it down the phone at him. But she had been so mortified when she'd realised he must have heard the things Corinne had been saying that she hadn't been able to help herself, knowing he must surely think her a wimp—besotted with him! And, if he found out that she had conceived after her rash behaviour with him last time, he'd think her even more of a fool now.

Which she was, she reminded herself with unsparing criticism. Not only for being weak-willed enough to let him break down all her defences, which had led to her winding up in bed with him, but for not even considering that she might not be adequately protected when she had vowed all those years ago that she would never let any man affect her enough for anything like this to happen again. And now here she was, eight years on, older but certainly no wiser. Not only in the same situation, but with the same man!

There were no calls for her when she returned to the office

with her head throbbing, her emotions in turmoil. At least, none from Seth, she was surprised to discover.

Perhaps he had given up trying to get hold of her and had simply gone back to enjoying himself with Corinne, Grace thought bitterly, although it didn't make her feel any better to imagine him stewing over what she had told him. If he had any conscience at all, he had to be! And privately, too, because she couldn't imagine for one moment that he'd discuss it with Corinne.

Or perhaps he would.

Piercingly she remembered the things that he and Corinne had said to make her fling the news of her pregnancy down the phone at him. Perhaps they had continued to discuss her afterwards. Perhaps even now he was taking solace in Corinne's arms.

As she moved around her office, trying to maintain her usual degree of efficiency and failing miserably, she was unable to imagine Corinne not taking exception to her stupendous lover sleeping with another woman. And, not just another woman, her late husband's granddaughter! Although, knowing Corinne, if Seth did tell her he was fathering a child she might even congratulate him on his virility!

Would he make love to the model, put his inconvenient mistake with Grace out of his mind until he returned next week? she wondered torturously. Because wouldn't this unplanned pregnancy be the ultimate revenge as far as he was concerned?

Angry tears stung her eyes as her head continued to pound and it was very late in the day when Simone, aware that her boss was feeling under the weather, came into the office to help Grace find a file that she had misplaced.

When the phone buzzed on the desk and Simone took the call, she said in a dumbfounded whisper to Grace, 'It's Seth. And he's in a hell of a mood.'

'Tough,' Grace responded flatly from the filing cabinet,

still determined not to speak to him. 'I'll talk to him when he gets back.''

'You're damn right you will!'

Both women's heads swivelled round to meet his implacable authority in the doorway. That uncompromising masculinity was only intensified by the white-hot anger in his face as he ordered, 'Simone—out! *Now!*'

The PA didn't stay to be told a second time. Distractedly it registered with Grace that the call that had come through from Reception must have been to warn her that the new CEO had just thundered in.

Her mood, though, matched his as, determined not to be intimidated by him, she snapped, 'Don't you ever come in here and speak to me or my PA like that again!'

'And don't you ever dare to deliver a blow like that closing remark you made this morning and then think you can just put the phone down on me!'

'Why not? Did it cramp your style with Corinne?' His face blanched with fury, but she was angry too. Very angry. 'Well, I'm very sorry to have dragged you back from such adoring company!'

She was near to tears but strove to control them, realising that he could only have used the executive jet to get back here so fast. He'd probably flown it himself, she thought waspishly, remembering his PA telling her once that he was an experienced pilot in his own right.

He moved angrily past her, grabbing her raincoat from the coat stand.

'Here. Take this. We're leaving.'

She only obeyed because her head was throbbing too much to endure a shouting match with him in the office, and because an imperious hand at her elbow was already urging her towards the door.

'Where are you taking me?'

'Somewhere where we can be alone.'

Every cell in her body rebelled against it, although her heart was beating with a wild anticipation that left her despairing with herself.

She caught Simone's discreet glance up at them as Seth marched her past her PA's desk, but she was too keyed up to argue with him or to say anything to Simone.

With his jaw set in stone, Seth summoned the lift, saying nothing as he urged her out of the building to the waiting Mercedes.

'Where are we going?' she demanded to know, as Seth handed her into the back of the car and slid in beside her. 'What makes you think you can just march into my office and start trying to take control of my life?'

The transparent screen closing in front of them obliterated any chance of their being heard by the man who was just pulling the car away.

'I would have thought that was obvious. You're having my child. Much as that must be the last thing that you, or either of us, wanted, I think that gives me some rights.'

He couldn't have made it any plainer than that!

Although, she'd known her pregnancy would be the last thing he'd want or expect, hearing him say it cut as painfully as scaling a wall of broken glass, and she turned away from him to hide the anguish scoring her face.

'I'm sorry,' he said, but coldly, tersely, noticing the pain of rejection in her tight, tense profile. 'I really believed you were on the Pill. It was wrong of me to assume.'

'Yes, it was,' she bit back with her eyes fixed on the headrest in front of her. If he'd used protection too, then this would never have happened, would it? she reasoned bitterly.

'And you weren't involved?' he challenged thickly before she could go on to explain that she wasn't as irresponsible as he obviously thought she was. 'You weren't the one writhing and sobbing beneath me in that bed?'

With flame colour touching her cheeks, Grace darted a

glance towards the thick neck of the man in front of the glass screen, immensely grateful that he couldn't hear what was being said.

Seth's graphic reminder of the way she had welcomed his love-making until she was begging for him to take her that night, though, shamed her into responding, 'I don't know what *you've* got to be so angry about. Anyway, I *was* on the Pill—or supposed to be.'

'So what happened?' His brows came together over eyes that were interrogative, darkly accusing. 'Did you forget to take it or something?'

'No, I didn't! I'd had a bout of tummy trouble just before we—' She couldn't even bring herself to say it. And because his attitude and his insinuation that it was all her fault was only making her feel worse than she did already, she threw angrily back at him, 'I'm not any happier about this than you are. And I'm sorry if it's messed up whatever you had planned with Corinne, but you needn't worry—I've got no plans to try and trap you!'

'Will you shut up?' It was a soft yet unmistakable command. 'For heaven's sake! Isn't it possible for you to utter one civil word to me unless you're being kissed?'

Turning her head sharply away from him, Grace stared sightlessly through the tinted glass at the surging bodies moving past the endless shops with their 'sale' signs splashed across the windows. She tried not to remember the ecstasy of that firm, male mouth covering hers, the mind-blowing pleasure as it had rediscovered her body like a familiar map, reading it with the deftness of a skilled explorer, recognising every secret curve and dip he had made his own.

'I swore,' she railed at herself. 'I swore I'd never let myself get pregnant—'

Again, she nearly said, but stopped herself in time, cupping her hands over her face with an exasperated sigh.

'It happens.' His voice was low, clipped, matter-of-fact.

'Not to me.' Inhaling deeply, Grace leaned back against the plush cushion of the headrest, closing her eyes against the truth.

Because that was just it—it did happen to her. *Twice.* Twice in her life she had gone the whole way with a man, and only one man. And twice in her life she had conceived, as though something beyond herself was determined that she would be impregnated with his seed. As though her ultimate function in life was to be the mother of his child.

'I expect every woman who finds herself in the same situation without wanting to be probably says the same thing.'

Yes, but they aren't having a baby with a man who doesn't even like them. Whose only reason for making love to them in the first place was just to exact some sort of revenge!

Noticing the increasing tension in the tight line of her jaw, Seth could see that this thing had come as an appalling shock to her, much as it had come as a complete shock to him. She looked now as she had looked the night they had made love and he had queried the possibility of her getting pregnant—like having his child was the last thing she could bear to contemplate. Which it probably was, he thought.

Because of her very high-profile affairs and the way she had treated him originally, he'd believed that to a girl like her men were just things to provide amusement, but in that, at least, he was beginning to realise he'd been wrong. The things Corinne had let slip about her had amazed him, even if he did suspect that they had been disclosed solely to reduce her step-granddaughter's possible appeal to him and boost her own sexual appeal in his eyes.

But in fact it had had the opposite effect. The knowledge that he could turn the haughty little enchantress who dumped men for a pastime, and who was really as cold as a Siberian winter, into a mass of steaming, sultry passion when he got her between the sheets had given him a shameful, chauvinistic satisfaction. Just how pliable did that make her in his hands? he wondered with a rush of masculine hormones raising the level of his libido a few notches. Because there was no doubt that she did things to him that no other woman had ever done.

Just thinking about how she responded to him in bed made him burn with the need to feel her nails digging into his back, to have her crying out his name—and only his—as they drove each other wild until they were sated. It didn't cool his ardour much to tell himself that it was because of his raging hormones where she was concerned that they were in this situation now. But the simple fact was that she *was* pregnant…

'Well, after what I heard Corinne saying on the phone…' he began, with his voice thickened by desire, 'I don't think I need even question whether it's mine, need I?'

As the Mercedes took a sharp left-hand turn that tipped Grace nearly into his lap, shame and humiliation leaped like angry flames to scorch her pride.

'You bastard!' Automatically her hand flew up and was instantly dealt with by a stronger one before it could make contact with his cheek.

Deftly she found herself pressed back against the cream leather upholstery with that long, lean body angled across hers.

'Believe it or not, it was meant as a compliment,' he breathed with menacing softness.

'Some compliment!' It came out on a squeak as excitement ripped through her, her senses leaping into overdrive from the hard, arousing weight of his body. Trying to collect her thoughts, she guessed it would be a major boost to his ego to realise he was the only lover she had ever had. But if he knew that then she would be lost, she thought despairingly, his to do whatever he wanted with, because she would have no defence then against his devastating sexual magnetism.

'Don't believe all Corinne tells you,' she got out tremulously, because he hadn't moved. He was still holding her captive as if he didn't trust her not to fly at him the instant he let her go. Or maybe he just liked being in control…

The need to assert command over her own actions had her wriggling against it.

He merely laughed at her ineffectual struggling. 'I won't, if you promise not to,' he said, letting her go.

'Promise not to what?' she quavered, even though he was sitting back on his own side of the car again now.

'Believe everything that Corinne Culverwell says.'

His tone was less than complimentary at the woman with whom he had supposedly shared a recent spell of unfettered passion. So what was he implying? Grace wondered with a leap of hope that made her despair at her own weakness in wanting to believe anything he might chance to tell her. That he really had gone to Madeira just to finalise a deal, as he had assured her he had on the phone that morning?

And if she believed that she would believe anything! she thought, realising that she was in very grave danger of trusting him—at least where his integrity was concerned.

The Mercedes pulled up at the kerbside and Seth handed her out onto the pavement. A young family passed them, a mother pushing a toddler in a buggy, a child of about four riding piggyback on the shoulders of the man beside her. They were all laughing, at ease with one another; happy.

Moments later Seth was guiding Grace through the foyer of one of London's most exclusive apartment-blocks. Chandeliers glittered, silver shone from highly polished surfaces, catching the reflection of a massive floral-display in the centre of the main area, while Grace's pumps sank into a carpet as soft as manicured grass.

This sort of luxury wasn't new to her. She had been born to it and had been accustomed to it until Culverwells' diminishing fortunes had meant everyone having to tighten their belts. But the young man with the motorbike who had had to drag himself out of virtual poverty had to have striven hard for this type of living—the cars, the plane, the power. Unbelievably so. She couldn't help but be impressed and a little overawed by the drive and determination he must have had to bring it about.

Nevertheless, as he brought her up in a lift with mirrored walls and they stepped out into a luxurious suite of rooms on the top floor of the building, she murmured, 'Trying to impress me, Seth? What are you trying to prove? That you've done well for yourself?'

His mouth pulling down on one side, he gestured for her to precede him into a huge room with deep pale sofas and panoramic views of their great city, which at this time of day was a glittering universe of twinkling lights. 'I don't think I need to do that. I leave proving to lawyers and those whose job it is to provide us with our daily bread. But, yes, I have done well.'

'And you're flaunting it for all you're worth.' His droll comment lent a curve to her mouth, though, and she realised that what she had just said wasn't totally true. Though the sumptuous drawing room in which he was inviting her to sit down was well-appointed, it was also uncluttered and exuded an air of understated elegance that was both tasteful and refreshing.

'What did you prefer, Grace—my being poor and totally at your mercy?'

Her eyelids pressed against the dark wells of her eyes as she sank down into the sofa's cushioning softness. Would he flay her with that for ever? It didn't make it any easier that her head felt as though it was splitting in two.

That rough edge to his voice, however, made her wonder if he meant at her mercy *emotionally*, until she realised how dangerous it was to think like that. Seth Mason was hard. He only meant at the mercy of the circumstances that getting involved with her had got him into.

'And you think,' she said feebly, looking painfully up at him, 'That by getting me pregnant you've got me at yours?'

His soft leather shoes made only a light sound over the varnished floor. 'You aren't at my mercy, Grace. Just at the mercy of your inability to resist whatever this thing is between us. Just as I am.' The curl of his mouth was self-mocking. 'And right now, yes, you are carrying my child. But don't worry. The situation can be easily remedied.'

She jumped up, and wished she hadn't when her head felt as though it had just exploded. Even so, that didn't stop her tossing back, 'That's about the sort of reasoning I'd expect from you! If you think I'm going to simply take the easy way out just because you can't bear to think of your *enemy* presenting you with a baby—wasn't that what you said we were the day you took over the company? *Enemies?*—you've got another thing coming! I don't want anything from you beyond a little recognition that you're its father. You can play around with whoever you want to, just so long as you acknowledge that. It makes no difference to me.'

'On the contrary.' His slow stride over the immaculate floor was measured, predatory. 'I find your being pregnant with my child rather satisfying.'

Whatever she had been expecting, it wasn't that.

'Why?' she asked guardedly. 'Because you think it would be one in the eye for the Culverwells to have to acknowledge your offspring as one of theirs?'

She meant because of the desire he'd been nursing all these years to avenge his family for the way they had suffered. Too late, though, she realised how it had sounded, as if he'd be tainting the pedigree blood of her family with the questionable origins of his.

For a moment his eyes blazed, but then his lashes came down and something like self-satisfaction shaped that hard mouth as he said, 'If it pulls you down off that class-conscious cloud you're obviously still clinging to, then, yes, I can't deny that it's a rather ironic twist of fate—don't you think?'

Because he hated snobbery, Grace knew, as much as she did now, although she knew she could never convince him of that in a million years.

'And you will have something from me, Grace. I'm not asking you to take the easy way out. In fact, I strictly forbid you to do anything that would harm our child. No, we're going to assume responsibility for this little one's life—together. And that means a marriage licence.'

'A marriage licence?' She was staring at him, wide-eyed with shock, her heart seeming to stand still. 'You can't be serious?'

There was no humour in his face as he advised, 'Believe me, I've never been more serious about anything in my life. There's no way any child of mine will grow up without the close presence of a father in its life.'

'As you did.'

'And as you did, I believe. After what Corinne told me about your own father deserting you, I'm surprised you'd even consider denying your own child that right.'

She had never talked about her father to Corinne, so the woman had obviously gleaned that information from Lance Culverwell.

'Well, you certainly had a good chin-wag about me, the pair of you, didn't you?' she accused in a wounded voice.

Seth's grimace said it all. Her grandfather's widow was garrulous enough without any help from him.

Amazingly, in spite of everything, some deep-boned intuition told Grace that Seth Mason would never be a party to idle gossip, and once again she found herself coming to believe that his dealings with Corinne were purely professional.

'The fact remains,' he said, 'that you were abandoned by your father, and through whatever circumstances he scarcely figured in your life. Don't let that happen to your own baby.'

Her head was banging so much she was beginning to feel sick; she didn't feel up to having this conversation with him.

Still trying to come to terms with the fact that he had actually proposed, unable to quite believe it, she said quickly, 'A lot of women manage perfectly well as single parents today.'

A shoulder moved beneath the superb tailoring of his jacket. 'It's up to you, but I'd like to think that you wouldn't be that selfish.'

When he was prepared to marry a woman he didn't love for the protection and well-being of his child.

'You make me feel I have no choice,' she uttered, feeling the strands of a silken web being slowly but insidiously woven around her.

'You do have a choice. I'm just asking you to make the right one.' A few lithe steps brought him within heart-stopping distance of her. 'Oh, come on, Grace.' His voice was soft, sultry, deep, like a jungle cat purring. 'It won't be so bad.' The fingers suddenly lifting her chin up, compelling her to look at him, were excruciatingly tender. 'Maybe I'm not the lawyer-doctor-accountant type you've always dreamed you'd be marrying.' *As if!* she thought almost hysterically. 'But we've got something that will ensure that any union between us will never be dull.'

He meant in bed.

A wave of excitement curled along her veins, a silent betrayal by her body of all it wanted—no, *needed*—from him, no matter how strongly her brain tried to deny the fact.

The shock and emotion were too much for her in her present state. As the room seemed to go wavy before her eyes, she dropped her head into her hands with an involuntary little groan, trying to stave off the threatening nausea.

She heard the low invective Seth uttered and could do nothing to resist the arms that were sweeping her effortlessly off her feet. 'Why didn't you tell me you weren't feeling well?' he scolded softly.

Caught against his hard, warm strength, her mind and body reeling with myriad sensations, somehow Grace managed a pained little smile. 'You only seemed concerned with what was going to happen to your baby.'

Those masculine lips curled in self-derision. 'Believe it or not, I do have a vested interest in its mother, too.'

He carried her through into the quiet luxury of the master bedroom. Compared to hers it was a sanctum of modern living, from the sinking carpet that bore his silent, effortless steps, to the monstrous bed with its very masculine but state-of-the-art cushions and covers that he dragged aside before setting her down on the dark-burgundy sheet covering the mattress.

Helping her out of her coat and jacket and then stooping to remove her shoes, he pressed her gently back on the pillow and pulled the duvet up around her.

'If you want anything,' he told her quietly, 'I'll be in the next room.' The degree of solicitude behind that simple statement brought a painful lump to her throat.

'A vested interest', he had said, but only because she was having his baby. He didn't care about her for herself. So why was she letting herself imagine such depth of emotion in his voice?

Nevertheless, no matter how much he had wanted to hurt her and her family, she thought, there was no doubt that he would accept his paternal responsibilities. The hardship and the poverty he had endured as a child and then, thanks to her, as a young man desperate to support the family who had taken him in, had obviously contributed to his determination not to let any child of his suffer in the same way. Although, even without that, there was no question in Grace's mind that he would still have held the same view about being a seriously hands-on parent. But was she prepared to let him help her bring up her child? Marry him? Apprehension coupled with excitement didn't do much to ease the painful banging in her head.

If she didn't, she reflected, and she decided to go it alone, there was no way that her child would go without seeing its father at regular intervals; Seth would demand that, of course, and she wouldn't try and stop him seeing his child—no matter how much it might hurt her to have to face him on a personal level from time to time, because she didn't think she would be able to carry on working with him after this. Her child would never want for anything financially. But was that enough?

She remembered how it had felt growing up. Her grandparents had been wonderful, had given her everything she could have wanted. But, guiltily, sometimes she had missed the fun and activities that her school friends seemed to have with their parents—particularly their fathers—younger, more energetic adults who could get involved in a game of tennis with them, or chase after them before scooping them high into the air shrieking with laughter, as fathers always seemed to be able to do. Fathers who were always there and didn't disappear for months, or even years, on end. She had missed having a birth mother, of course, but she had missed her father more than she could ever put into words, because she had known he was around somewhere. Just not with her. And that had hurt more than she had ever dared to let herself accept.

She thought of the little family she had noticed on the way up here. Two children. Two parents. A happy balance. She owed her child that much, didn't she? And if—*fingers crossed*—this little one growing inside her went to its full term, was born safely…

Fear threatened to rise like a dark spectre, but she fought it back. She couldn't—wouldn't—let herself think about that now, for the same reason she hadn't been able to bring herself to tell Seth what had happened before. It was a part of her life that she wasn't particularly proud of and she had paid for it dearly—then pressed it so far to the back of her mind that it was as though that girl she had been and everything that had happened to her had happened to someone else. It wouldn't help her or him in any way, she reasoned with a kind of muddled logic, to dig it all up now.

So with the muted tones of Seth's voice conducting business over the phone in the other room, and the elusive scent of him surrounding her in his personal bedding, she made her decision, safe in the knowledge that whatever his feelings towards her he would always be there to love and support his child. And that was all that mattered, she told herself resolutely. Wasn't it?

CHAPTER EIGHT

ABSENTLY Grace toyed with the slim gold band on her finger, noticing how brilliantly it shone in the high Mediterranean sun.

'What's the problem Mrs Mason? Still having difficulty digesting it?' Propped up on an elbow on the sun deck of his luxurious yacht, wearing only a pair of dark bathing briefs, his bronzed body slick with oil, Seth was watching her where she lay sunbathing on her back on the soft mattress beside him. His face was alight with teasing. 'Perhaps I'd better give you another dose of something to make it slide down more easily.' His eyes gleamed wickedly as he leant closer to her, his black hair falling forward. 'Or slide up,' he murmured tantalisingly in her ear in a way specifically designed to arouse her, as he had been doing, much to her shaming delight, for the past five days.

She still couldn't quite believe it had taken less than seven weeks from that evening in his apartment, when he had practically demanded they get married, to lying here with him in nothing but the lower half of her shimmering blue bikini. She was unable to get enough of his hands and lips on her body, her deliciously tender nipples already hardening in anticipation of his special therapy, that secret place at the apex of her thighs contracting, burning for him, because he hadn't made love to her for at least two hours.

When she rolled over onto her stomach so that he wouldn't recognise the naked need in her face, the betrayal of her shamelessly aroused body, he laughed knowingly and moved to draw a slow, sensuous line with a finger over the sensitive length of her spine, creating havoc in her as his hand ran caressingly over the smooth, silky mound of her buttocks, temptingly enhanced by the separating blue string at their crease.

'Don't think you can pretend modesty after all that we've done,' he mocked softly against the nape of her neck, causing a pleasurable shudder to shake her still slender body as she thought of the shocking intimacies they had shared since their wedding night—the way he had shown her how to please him, things that she would never have imagined herself doing to any man, but which had only enhanced the pleasure for her too.

'I think from now on you'd better leave these off,' he advised as he peeled her bikini bottom away from her slick, hot body like a sybarite unwrapping an epicurean feast.

Exposed, open to his probing hands and eyes, she squirmed beneath him like a restless filly, groaning into the pillow, a sound both of sensuous delight and defeat. Her excitement was only heightened as he breathed, thrillingly aware, 'I'm sorry. I forgot how reluctant you always are to do this with me,' and pulled her round onto her back to accept her fate.

Much later, lying in the darkness in the big bed in the master cabin, tender in several places after a long evening of making love, Grace marvelled at the iron control that Seth had exercised during the weeks leading up to their marriage—whenever since he had shown himself to be not only a sensational lover, but an insatiable one. too.

After agreeing to be his wife—but only, as she had made clear to him to deflect him from her true feelings, for the sake of their child—she had resolved to refuse to move in with him before the wedding, had he asked her to. But he hadn't. Nor had he even attempted to get her into his bed.

Perhaps he had been busy saying goodbye to his glorious bachelorhood and the women who'd currently figured in his life. *Like Corinne*, she'd thought painfully, although she had refused to dwell on any relationship he might have had with her grandfather's beautiful widow then, and she refused to do so now.

She still wasn't totally sure whether Corinne Culverwell was anything other than a business associate, as Seth had first implied she was, although the reason he had given for being on Corinne's yacht that day in Madeira had been borne out a few days later during a telephone call she'd taken from one of his colleagues. He had unknowingly confirmed what Seth had said, that it had been purely to tie up some loose ends with the takeover, since it was on the way back from the neighbouring Canary Islands where he'd been spending Christmas and New Year with his family. As to any previous intimacies he might have had with the model, Grace had no intention of questioning him further. If she did, she decided, then he might realise the truth—that his new and reluctant bride was already dangerously in love with him. Dangerous to *her*, that was, because she knew full well that he wouldn't have married her if she hadn't been carrying his child.

As for the way he was with her in bed…

Well, he was only behaving the way any healthy, red-blooded male at the peak of his fitness would behave with any reasonably good-looking woman who had given him licence to her body, wasn't he? she reminded herself. Although deep down she was beginning to realise that he was as enslaved by his desire for her as she was by her own for him.

He was attentive in public, too, practically proprietorial—something that Corinne, only recently informed about the baby, had commented on at the wedding.

'Well, you're both a pair of dark horses, aren't you?' she

had remarked in that affectedly polished voice with a smile that left her long green eyes cold, her brightly painted lips stretched falsely wide as she caught Grace momentarily alone. 'You do know how much you'll have to give to please a man like that, don't you?' Jealousy was stamped all over Corinne's beautiful face, though she was battling to hide it and failing miserably. Grace had felt almost sorry for her. 'I really think you might have bitten off more than you can chew this time, sweetheart. He's behaving like he owns you already.'

'Don't I?' Seth had enquired, overhearing, looking dynamic in a pale-grey suit, white shirt and silver tie. He'd turned around from the little group of guests he had been talking to and had slipped an arm around Grace, studying the slender hand he caught in his and which bore his shiny new ring.

Fresh from the register office in her short and simple white sixties-style smock dress, with a sprinkling of white flowers interwoven in her pale, elegantly swept-up hair, Grace had worried that there was more behind his supposedly teasing question than he'd been letting show. A hard arrogance that had said he had her where he wanted her—her master in the office and a soon-to-be-willing plaything in his bed.

It had been a pleasant enough day, in spite of that. At Grace's request, and in view of the relatively short time for arranging everything, it had been a small and very private wedding away from the prying eyes of the press, with only very close friends and family members attending, with Beth and an old friend of Seth's as witnesses. The reception had been a simple affair, too, held in the palm court of one of the West End hotels.

'Grace, I think it's time you met my mother.'

Seeing the grey-haired, tired-looking but straight-backed lady in the moss-green dress and jacket, waiting with a much younger, copper-haired woman as they arrived at the hotel, Grace allowed Seth to lead her across to them, her heart coming up into her mouth.

He hadn't seen fit to take her to meet his foster mother during those few weeks before they were married, and it hadn't taken long for Grace to realise why: this was the woman who had cared for him since he'd been a young teenager until he had been forced to leave home when Lance Culverwell had had him sacked from that boatyard. It was because of her, Grace, and the way she had led Seth on, practically seducing him on that beach and then unknown to him conceiving his child, that her grandfather had made him pay. He had used his influence to crush him, deprive him of his livelihood, splitting the family up and causing them unnecessary hardship when Seth had left town to try to find work elsewhere. But Nadia Purvis, as she was introduced to Grace, couldn't have accepted her son's new bride with a warmer greeting as she kissed Grace on both cheeks and welcomed her into the family circle, putting Grace instantly at ease.

'I apologise for not having been able to meet you before now,' her new mother-in-law said. 'But we've been on a trip to Canada and the Rockies—a present from Seth for my birthday.' The way she looked up at him showed nothing but gratitude and immense pride for the tall dark man to whom she had once given a home—and a lot of love too, Grace knew without being told. 'My special birthday.' Her weary eyes were bright with laughter as she turned back to Grace, making them all laugh with her as she added, 'Although I'm not saying which one. Then we finished up in New England visiting Alvin—'

'My twin,' the long-haired beauty who had been waiting patiently beside her chipped in. 'He's at uni there. We're supposed to be identical but fortunately, I'm happy to say, not in every way.'

Grace laughed again, as the others did, deciding that the girl couldn't have been much older than twenty. 'I'm Alicia, by the way.'

Taking the bangled hand that was being offered, Grace

leant forward and kissed her. 'Hello, Alicia.' And then, as recollections kicked in, she was murmuring before she realised it, 'Aren't you...?' and only managed to stop herself in time.

Of course. That day all those years ago. Hand in hand, sated with love-making, Seth had taken her back to a modest little house on the edge of the woods. She hadn't gone in. He had only taken her there to give her a lift back home on the bike. But as she'd been putting on her helmet a little girl had come running out of the house. A little girl in pyjamas who had begged him to take her for a ride, and whose bright curls he had ruffled before gently but firmly sending her packing back inside.

Amazingly, it seemed that Seth hadn't told his mother just who had been responsible for him losing his job at the boatyard, and secretly she could only thank him for that. But then it only bore out what he had always maintained—that it wasn't his style to kiss and tell. Even when he had been humiliated and demoralised he hadn't stooped to smearing her or her family's name. Instead he had kept it to himself with that private and very personal resolution of one day making them pay...

'You're Seth's sister,' she finished now, amending what she had been going to say, and guessing that the word "foster" would have been dropped from this family's vocabulary a long time ago.

'And the baby of the family,' Seth added, 'as she was born fifteen minutes after her brother. And consequently indulged and spoiled beyond belief.'

'But not by you.' Big hazel eyes twinkled mischievously up at the elder brother whom she obviously adored and who had been around for most of Alicia's young life. Grace calculated that the twins must only have been about two years old when Seth had entered their world. 'Although he *has* said he's going to buy me a BMW convertible if I do well in my exams. I'm doing interior design,' she clarified for Grace's sake.

'He's said nothing of the sort,' Seth denied, though with that charming smile of his, obviously used to Alicia's ploys to try and twist him round her little finger.

'And you better had do well, young lady,' her mother warned. 'After all it's costing him to put you through that college.'

Grace laughed again, liking his sister, liking them all, and wishing with all her heart that this marriage had been one built on love, trust and respect. But an exchange of glances with her new husband showed no more than a fervid desire for her within the closed, inscrutable depths of his eyes.

'I'm sorry my younger son couldn't be with you,' Nadia was saying to Grace. 'But he's in the middle of very important exams, too, although he does send his apologies.'

He had also sent a huge bouquet of mixed roses and a congratulatory telegram that morning which was now displayed, with the simple bouquet of lilies she had carried that morning, on either side of the two-tiered wedding cake. 'Exams are very important,' Grace commented, guessing that Seth was probably funding the best possible education for Alicia's twin brother too, a thing he himself had been deprived of. She had recently learned he had studied long and hard, way into the night, after he had left school.

Simone joined them then with her accountant husband, breaking up the intimate little party, and some time afterwards Alicia came and looped her arm through Grace's, asking her about her gallery. Grace was happy to discover that they shared surprisingly similar tastes in art.

Not long after the cake had been cut and a toast made by Seth's best man, Seth ushered Grace away to the airport, from where they flew out to the Mediterranean island and Seth's private yacht to begin their three-week honeymoon.

'I thought it might be more to your liking than that crude

little boat I made the mistake of thinking I could first woo you on,' he remarked, as he lifted her through the sliding doors on the bough into the vessel's luxurious saloon, where a champagne dinner was waiting for them. But his tone had been cynical and self-derisive, so she responded with a slightly defensive edge to her own voice as he set her down on her feet.

'As a matter of fact, I loved that little dinghy. It was simple and honest. Uncomplicated.' Not like this floating temple to wealth and success that screamed of his power and influence, and was bigger and more luxurious than anything her family had ever owned.

'Uncomplicated?' His laugh expressed something not far short of disdain. 'I suppose something about that day had to be.'

'I meant real. Unpretentious.' She struggled to explain, trying not to let the scorn that still festered inside him get to her, to spoil the day. She wasn't able to keep the regret out of her voice as she said it, though, and realised, with an ache of remorse in her chest, that she had let him know that eight years too late.

They returned to England and moved into Seth's apartment on a sunny spring day that was still rather cool after the kinder climate of the Mediterranean. The place had been cleaned and aired by a discreet staff and there was a 'welcome home' bouquet, professionally arranged in a clear glass vase on the dining room table, from Nadia.

There was a card, too, among their post, sent jointly from the twins, which from the postmark, Grace smilingly noted, had obviously been chosen, signed and posted by Alicia. Even Corinne rang to welcome them home, but not until the following evening, because she had forgotten on which day they were supposed to be coming back.

'And how's my step-granddaughter?' she asked in that

too-perfectly-English voice, then punctuated her question with a very audible shudder. 'Don't you just hate it when people refer to us like that? I do. It makes me sound so…*ancient*,' she announced, and without waiting for Grace to answer any of her questions went on to enquire, 'so how's that gorgeous husband of yours?'

'Fit,' Grace responded, smiling to herself. Corinne was like a runaway train when she got going. 'And disgustingly tanned! He's out at the moment.'

'What, already?'

Grace sighed to herself, wondering why she was always left wishing she hadn't said things that Corinne could pounce on.

'He's at a meeting involving one of his own companies. Some emergency or other.'

'And it's obviously too early in your marriage to ask if you believe him.' Corinne gave an affected little giggle. 'I must admit, I never imagined a man like Seth Mason tying himself down to one woman. Not after what he said to me, not too long ago, when I asked him if he was ever going to settle down with anyone.'

'Don't tell me—he said no?'

'No, he didn't actually. All he said was that if he ever chose to marry anyone it would be because of mutual benefit to them both.'

Mentally, Grace shrugged. 'So, he was cynical about marriage. A lot of people are.'

'Possibly. Who knows what goes on in any man's mind? I do think, though, that you were part of his long-term plan.'

'Plan?' Grace was beginning to feel decidedly uneasy.

'Oh, come on, Grace, you're a prize for any man. You have to see that. Particularly to one who's had to drag himself up from the bottom of the heap. Clever move on his part, getting you pregnant so you'd marry him. He certainly doesn't believe in dilly-dallying, does he?'

'What exactly are you saying, Corinne?' Grace was holding the phone so tensely that her fingers were beginning to hurt. 'Are you accusing Seth of deliberately seducing me just so he could…?' Little doubts were creeping into her mind as to how much truth there was in what Lance Culverwell's widow was saying. Stupid doubts, but doubts nevertheless.

'Not accusing, my little innocent.' Grace cringed at the condescending phrases Corinne was too keen on using whenever she spoke to her. 'I'm applauding him. I'm sure he's madly in love with you, but you must admit that having Grace Tyler beside him won't do him any harm socially, either. What with all your high-flying contacts and upper-crust connections, the man can't fail to get where he's going—and fast.'

Corinne was only saying these things, Grace was sure, because she was jealous of her. After all, Seth Mason had it all—looks, money, power—while Corinne had had to content herself with a man two and a half times her age to give her the type of lifestyle she obviously craved.

'Seth doesn't need anyone to help him get where he's going,' Grace snapped, as much to convince herself as Corinne. 'And he certainly isn't interested in social climbing. He hates that sort of snobbery.'

'That's what we all say, but if the opportunity arises…' Grace could almost see the woman's expressive little gesture. 'And you did accuse him of being an opportunist, before you suddenly surprised us all by announcing you were having his baby and getting hitched to him.' Which wasn't quite how it had happened, Grace thought, but was feeling too unhappy to correct Lance Culverwell's widow.

'Our reason for getting married so soon—and he was as committed to this as I was—was to give our baby the best possible start.'

'That doesn't stop him from being the opportunist you obviously thought he was.'

Only because after we made love he seemed to vanish into

thin air! Because I thought he'd only been using me! Grace wanted to cry out, but realised that that would just endorse the things Corinne was saying.

'And you didn't marry my grandfather for personal gain?' The accusation slipped out before she could stop it.

'Oh, come on! I was very fond of your grandfather. I thought he was a poppet—you know that. But a girl's got to think of her future, too.'

'Well, you certainly succeeded there, Corinne.'

'Which is why I think I know the Seth Masons of this world much better than you do,' the woman persisted, too thick-skinned to be unduly affected by the things her late husband's granddaughter reproached her for. 'I'm not claiming to be a saint. I know I've got my faults. And I really don't want to see you get hurt.' Poor Corinne; she really believed that, Grace thought bitterly. 'But let's face it. You've got a hell of a good deal too, haven't you? I mean, he's got to be *incredible* in bed.' It would dawn on Grace later that for the model to surmise about Seth's mind-blowing prowess as a lover meant that Corinne could have done nothing more than fantasise about sleeping with him. 'And what's wrong with allowing somebody to use you just a little if your reward is mind-blowing sex with a man who looks and sounds like that?'

After Corinne rang off, Grace speculated unhappily on all that the woman had told her. Had Seth really been so keen to propose because of the personal gains he believed he could make by marrying her?

She was sure that first and foremost he had the interests of his baby at heart, but had he also seen her as a way of furthering his brilliant career, as Corinne had so unkindly suggested? Had that supposedly unselfish act to do what was right by her and the baby masked a mercenary streak that allowed him to use his child's mother for his own ends? The mercenary streak that had driven him to take Culverwells from under her nose so humiliatingly? And he'd done it with Corinne's help, because without the model's compliance he'd never have succeeded in exacting revenge in quite the way he had.

The only positive point to come out of that telephone conversation with Corinne, Grace realised, was the confirmation that Seth had been telling the truth—that he and the model weren't, and apparently never had been, lovers. It was small consolation, though, after everything else that her grandfather's widow had said.

Her pregnancy had already begun to show. Grace knew there were whispered comments and wild speculation in the office about the exact timing of her baby's conception, but she deflected the surreptitious glances and casual remarks with her usual air of detachment and calm efficiency.

They had to wonder, though, she thought at the moments when unvoiced curiosity made her feel a little self-conscious, whether their new and dynamic CEO and Lance Culverwell's granddaughter had actually known each other before Seth had seized control of the company in that hostile bid. Or whether, having faced each other on opposite sides of the commercial battlefield, their determined new boss had broken through his pretty opponent's line of defence with guns blazing and had swept her up onto his charging steed and into his bed before she had time to realise what was happening.

Which was about the size of it, Grace couldn't help thinking, still plagued by doubts after that last conversation she had had with Corinne a couple of weeks ago. She wondered if those curious speculators were also silently applauding Seth Mason, as Corinne had, for what must look like a very shrewd move, in view of the antagonism and opposition he had been getting from her.

On the up side, her morning sickness seemed to have all but sorted itself out. Nor did she feel as tired as she had during the first weeks of her pregnancy. But her worries and suspicions about why Seth had actually married her were beginning to make her feel an emotional wreck.

She already knew that he didn't love her, that he had only married her to give her child his name. But, like every woman before her who had found herself in a similar situation, she was troubled by insecurities while nursing a desperate, if not completely vain, hope of making him love her.

That was until the day she found that photograph of herself with Paul.

It was the only snap she had kept of her fiancé because it featured her grandfather standing between them with an arm around them both. It had been taken shortly after they had got engaged.

She didn't realise Seth had come into the bedroom until he said over her shoulder in a voice that was frostily controlled, 'If you still want him, you only have to say.'

Startled, she dropped the photo back into the open drawer she had been sorting through, realising how guilty that must make her look even as she swung round to retort, 'Of course I don't want him. How could you possibly imagine that?' But he did, she realised, because ever since that day she had spoken to Corinne he had clearly sensed a change in her, once or twice even querying if anything was wrong.

His smile didn't warm the steely grey of his eyes, and the fingers that lifted lightly to her cheek were cold too, making her gasp. 'Then why are there tears glistening in your eyes?'

'They're not. I mean…'

Not because of that, she was trying to say. But she couldn't seem to form the words to tell him that it had been the picture of her grandfather looking fit and well that had brought on that spurt of emotion.

'And why, when I touched you, did you flinch?'

Her shoulders sagging, Grace realised that she was in a no-win situation. Seth Mason was a possessive and dominant male and wouldn't take being side-stepped by his wife for another man lightly—even if he didn't love her.

'Perhaps you *want* me to tell you I still want Paul, is that it?' she tossed up at him with disbelieving eyes, barely able to contain the hysterical little laugh that bubbled up in her throat from the absurdity of it all, but even more from the harrowing suspicion that she might just be right. Perhaps he *had* originally married her to suit his own ends but now, realising the enormity of what he had done, just wanted an easy way out.

'Do you?' he challenged again.

'If you believe that, then there's no hope for us, is there?' she murmured dismally. 'I married *you*, didn't I?'

'Yes.' His powerful chest expanded on a sharply drawn breath. 'You married me.' Not a glimmer of emotion moved those harshly sculpted features as he added, exhaling air from his lungs, 'And would you care to tell me why?'

Caught in the trap of her own making, Grace didn't know what to say.

Because I love you!

The admission, even in her own mind, made her go hot and cold. How hopelessly lost she would be if he realised that!

'Well, not for the same reason as you—obviously!' she hurled at him.

'And what would that be?' His narrowing eyes were glinting with anger.

'To open the doors you haven't actually managed to kick down yet.'

There, she had said it, thrown it in his face like a douse of cold water.

Deny it! her heart screamed, only he didn't.

He stood stock-still for a moment, like some cold, unfeeling statue frozen in time. But then a muscle twitched in his jaw, the only indication that there was life pulsing inside him, before he tilted his head in the briefest of acknowledgements.

'So we now know where we both stand, don't we?' he stated grimly, and walked away, his actions only reaffirming what she already knew. That he hadn't a scrap of feeling for her beyond the fact that she was going to be the mother of his child.

After that their marriage seemed to undergo a marked change. What comradeship there was started to ebb out of their relationship. Seth began to stay later at the office, often arranging for his car and driver to bring Grace home.

They seldom made love any more, sleeping back to back like strangers, and when they did it was with an almost antagonised passion, as though each resented the needs that only the other could supply.

Somehow Grace managed to keep up appearances in the office, particularly as Seth was conducting a lot of business outside of it for a lot of the time. When the weekends came she spent most of her Saturdays when he was away working helping Beth at the gallery, feeling lonely and confined in the apartment—for all its spacious luxury—when Seth wasn't there.

'We'll have to find somewhere else to live when the baby comes,' she suggested tentatively to him one morning when they were getting ready to leave for the office. They had made love the night before, a lengthy, wordless exchange of excruciating pleasure; it embarrassed her too much to even look at him as she recalled it, as it only seemed to accentuate his cold detachment this morning, emphasised by his hard executive image in the cold light of day. 'A child needs a garden to play in. Somewhere to run around and make a noise in without upsetting the neighbours.'

'Of course' was Seth's succinct response.

But then two days later he surprised her by coming home and tossing a pile of glossy brochures featuring ultra-superior properties down on the coffee table. Georgian mansions with acres of woodland; huge, modern split-level state-of-the-art glass houses, and one gothic-like stone building with gargoyles and turrets that also boasted its own lake.

'I'm sure you can find something in there to suit you,' he remarked.

'Any limit to the budget?' Grace enquired after a few moments, looking up from a page of homes with hair-raising price tags to see him casually shrugging out of his suit jacket. The sight of his broad shoulders beneath his white silk shirt and that tapering torso, spanned by the dark waistband of his trousers, caused a painful contraction in her throat.

'Let me worry about that,' he advised.

So she kept on browsing, and when she had finished she laid the last of the brochures back on the pile on the coffee table without a word.

'Well?' he enquired over the paper he was reading when she sank back against the creamy cushions of the sofa.

Grace wondered if her disillusionment showed in her face.

She couldn't tell him that looking at those houses had lowered her spirits. That she found them as cold and impersonal as he seemed to be with her the minute she was out of his bed.

Had success and power changed him so much from the home-loving, surprisingly tender young man she had given herself to all those years ago? she couldn't help wondering desolately. Did he just want money to flaunt at the type of people he believed deserved his contempt? Like her grandfather? Like the Paul Harringdales of this world? Like her?

'Perhaps something a little less…obvious,' she suggested, which sounded more gracious than calling the homes 'ostentatious' or 'depressing'. And, to put him more on the right track next time, she added a little coyly, 'If it helps, I prefer… simpler things.'

Surprisingly, to Seth it came as a revelation. But why

should it surprise him? it struck him now. There was the quiet, unfussy wedding she had readily agreed to. He'd thought it was because it had been something she merely wanted to get through for the sake of the baby. But would she still have wanted all that simplicity if they had been a love-struck couple? he wondered, because there were other things, too.

Most of the women he'd met in his life had been shopaholics, and he'd imagined she'd be the greatest, but in that he'd been proven wrong. She didn't particularly like shopping, not for clothes at any rate…and as for those artificial, glitzy parties they were constantly being invited to, amazingly she seemed to spurn them with a passion almost as strong as his own.

'Quite a woman of hidden depths, aren't you?' he commented dryly, joining her on the sofa.

'Does that surprise you?' Her eyes, instantly guarded as he came down beside her, had a rather wounded look about them. 'You thought you were marrying an inveterate snob.'

'Have I ever called you that?' Surely he hadn't? Even if at times, in view of how she had treated him in the past, he might have thought it.

'You didn't have to,' she murmured, adding to his sense of guilt.

'We all make mistakes,' he conceded.

'You?' That familiar scorn heightened the healthy colour in her cheeks. Now that her morning sickness had eased, she was really beginning to blossom. 'Surely not!'

In reply he merely lifted her hand, healthily golden against the darker bronze of his, and pressed it to his lips. Her skin was scented and soft.

Dark-blonde lashes came down as though she couldn't bear it—or what he could do to her, he decided with ruthless satisfaction, aware of her pulse beating frantically against the heel of his hand.

'I thought you were always right.' An edge had crept into

her voice, a tension caused by the sexual undercurrent that dominated everything they said and did. Would it destroy them eventually? he wondered. Because, when it was gone, what would there be left?

'Sometimes it isn't a bad thing to be wrong.'

A question darkened the blue around her dilated pupils, but he glanced down at the hand he still held to avoid a conversation he didn't want to get involved in, studying the simple arrangement of stones that formed her engagement ring.

Not for her the high-carat diamond he'd thought she might pick to cement their hurried betrothal. Or the extortionately priced yellow sapphires that the jeweller had tried to tempt her with in that exclusive goldsmith's in the West End.

Now his thumb brushed lightly over the modest cluster of tiny rubies and emeralds surrounding that single tiny diamond she had selected over all the rest.

Once again, he found himself silently admitting, this lovely girl whom circumstances had virtually forced him into a union with had, without even knowing it, tossed his preconceived ideas about her right back in his face. She was a mixture of simplicity and complexity and he could never tell which one of those facets of her character was going to reveal itself to him each day. The one who stayed reserved and distant from him while they were here like this or alone together in the office, or the one who staved off any suggestion of anything intimate with him for as long as she was able to, then turned into a tigress the instant he took matters into his own hands when they were in bed.

Then no words could deny that what they did together was meant to be—and what both of them wanted. They were from totally different worlds, universes, and yet in bed they spoke the same language, one that consisted only of touch and feel and the most basic of instincts, where only the most exclusively sensual phrases played any part.

He felt the need to speak that language with her now, and

knew that was something he could have fulfilled within seconds if he had taken it upon himself to do so. Because she
always responded to him; because she couldn't deny herself
the pleasure she craved from him any more than he could
resist the scent, taste and feel of her eager body beneath his
hands, the hypnotising sweetness of her incredible mouth.

An emotion, more complex and far less primal than the
need to have her, stirred inside him, threatening to make him
vulnerable to this beautiful woman who had once slain him
with just one look. He wasn't prepared to let that happen. Not
ever again.

'I'm sure we can find something to please you eventually,' he said dismissively, getting up, his voice sounding
strained and distinctly cold from the control he was having
to exercise in not tugging off those stuffy office clothes of
hers and whisking her off to bed to make love to her until she
was sobbing to take him into her. 'Until then we'll just have
to manage—if it's not too difficult for you.'

And on that note he turned and strode out of the room.

Everything was going as it should, Grace thought two or three
weeks later. At least with her pregnancy. The baby was devel-
oping normally, despite her initial fears, and the doctor had
said that, although they needed to keep an eye on her because
of her mother's and her own medical history, she was a prime
example of a healthy mother-to-be.

Everything would be perfect, she decided painfully, if the
man she had picked to fall in love with had been in love with
her. But he wasn't, and the knowledge that he might never
love her, coupled with the strain that that was putting on their
marriage, was making her snappy and irritable.

Only this week she had had two migraines and had had
to leave the office early. Seth had been away, and as she'd
been fine by the time he'd come back she hadn't bothered
mentioning it to him.

Now, though, sitting at her desk with another headache coming on, a pain in her lower abdomen and feeling decidedly yucky, Grace wound up the conversation she was having with a customer who was far too chatty and made a merciful escape to the bathroom.

There she made a discovery that left her trembling with shock and fear.

She was bleeding!

She was nearly five months pregnant and she had started a miscarriage!

CHAPTER NINE

SETH's face was flushed and he was breathing heavily as he burst into Grace's office.

He had been in a board meeting when Simone's call had come through and, too impatient and worried to wait for the lift, he had taken the stairs, flying down them like his life depended upon it.

With a nod at Simone who was just coming out, he crossed over to Grace, who was sitting with her feet up on the couch that stood against the far wall.

There was a deathly pallor to her face that concerned him immensely and her eyes as she looked up at him were dark with something closely akin to desperation. When he took her hand and dropped to his haunches beside her, he could feel how much she was shaking.

'What is it?' It was an anxious whisper as he closed both hands around the cool trembling one he was holding. 'Are you going to be all right for me?'

She looked at him as though she was almost surprised to hear him say that. 'Oh *Seth*...I think I'm losing our baby.' Tears mingled with the desperate emotion in her eyes, an emotion that tugged at him so much that he had to remind himself that it was purely maternal instinct that was making her look like that. They said it kicked in at some point of the pregnancy, however unwanted the child might have been to begin with.

'Hush. Don't upset yourself,' he breathed. He even managed a sort of watery smile. 'You need to conserve all your energy to help that little one hold on. And, anyway, it might not be a miscarriage.'

'It is. It's happening again!'

'Again?' Puzzlement joined the anxious lines scoring his face.

'Just like before.'

'Before when? What are you talking about, Grace? What do you mean? When has this happened before?'

Now she wished she hadn't kept it from him. 'I was pregnant,' she admitted, her shoulders drooping.

'When?' There was so much he didn't know about her, that he had only begun to find out since they were married. But this? When had she been pregnant? Whose child had she been carrying before his? He wanted to know all the answers—but now wasn't the time. Also, Simone was just coming back in.

'Is there anything else I can do for you both, Seth?' Over the weeks, since the brief engagement, Simone Phillips had become as firm a friend and colleague to him as she was to Grace.

Getting to his feet, Seth inhaled heavily. He had already had Simone send for a friend of his, a top gynaecologist with whom he played squash sometimes during the office lunch-breaks.

'Yes, you can put anything that needs handling urgently and which you aren't able to deal with yourself through to my PA's office. She'll know what to do.' Simone had already made Grace a cup of tea, he noticed. 'And perhaps you could see that we aren't disturbed.'

'Of course.'

When she had gone he pulled up a hard chair and sat astride

it, facing Grace. 'Now…' There was a marked hesitancy in his voice. 'Perhaps it's something you didn't want to tell me about, Grace, but in view of the circumstances…' His gaze dropped to the tell-tale mound of her abdomen beneath the overlap of her blouse which she was absently stroking, as though to protect the child she was so afraid of losing.

Their child.

But whose child had she carried and lost before? Had she loved him? Who before him had had such an important claim on her affections?

'It isn't what you think.' As she turned her face to his, he thought he had never seen anyone look more miserable.

His impenetrable gaze caused Grace to lower hers. She could tell what he was thinking and she couldn't bear it. It was enough that she might lose him if she lost the baby, but she couldn't bear to lose what precious little respect he had for her as well.

'It was eight years ago…after I came back to London. Neither of us had taken any precautions.'

'What are you saying?' His voice had dropped to a whisper and all the colour seemed to have seeped out of his olive skin. 'You mean, after we made love down there…?' He was shaking his head sharply as though trying to clear a blinding fog from in front of his eyes—eyes that were dark with disbelief. 'You *conceived*? You were pregnant with *my* child?'

She gave a sort of half-nod.

Now he could see why she had been so livid at finding out she was pregnant for a second time—and by him, a man she couldn't help surrendering to and yet for whom she had never entertained a moment's real feeling.

'We must be one hell of a fertile couple,' he remarked savagely. 'Why didn't you tell me? Why didn't you let me know?'

'At the time?' She sounded and looked sadly cynical. 'What

would you have done, married me? A girl you thought was only out for a good time?'

'Which was why I thought you'd be protected.' He was still shaking his head. 'I never dreamt you wouldn't be.'

'You seem to have made a habit of that.' And, in case he was thinking she'd been totally loose as well as irresponsible, she admitted, laying herself bare, 'It was my first time.'

To say he looked shocked would be an understatement, she thought, as those steely eyes widened and a flush washed up over those strong cheekbones.

He had been her first lover?

While he was still trying to get over one piece of unbelievable news, he was hit smack between the eyes with another.

Grace Tyler, the good-time girl—willing and eager for him without any inhibitions whatsoever—had been a virgin? Beneath the worry, his rampant concern for her, he knew a warming and very misplaced sense of macho pride.

'It wasn't obvious.'

She gave a pained little shrug. 'No. I've read it isn't always, if a girl's athletic or has done a lot of horse riding, which I had.'

'What happened?' he prompted, his eyes searching hers for enlightenment.

'I lost it.'

'How far into…?'

She swallowed. She didn't want to relive it—the pain and the misery, the feelings of isolation. And afterwards the months of depression and self-blame.

'Nearly five months.'

He swore under his breath, while his eyes closed from some inner frustration. With himself? she wondered. With her?

'Why didn't you tell me before? I mean…since?' His deep voice trembled with exasperation. 'We're man and wife, for goodness' sake!'

'I don't know. I treated you badly and I paid for it. It was a bad time in my life. I just wanted to put it behind me.' And, knowing now that it would be wrong to hold anything else back from him, because he was her husband, because he had a right to know and because—heaven help her!—because she loved him, she tagged on reluctantly, 'I was ill for quite some time.'

'Dear…!' He raised his eyes skywards, emitting some unrepeatable oath. 'All the more reason why, in view of your mother losing her life in childbirth, you should have told me,' he rebuked softly. 'And yet, knowing this, you kept it from me. Why?'

'I don't know.' Because it was all in the past. It couldn't happen again. *Dear heaven!* she prayed. *Don't let it happen again.* 'I was shocked and angry when I realised I was pregnant again. I couldn't believe it was happening to me. I'm sorry.' It had been stupid of her; she knew that now.

Turning to him, squeezing the strong hand clasping hers like it was a lifeline, she breathed, 'Oh Seth! What am I going to do?'

There was real fear in her eyes, and for once in his life Seth felt totally helpless. If anything happened to her, or to the baby, or both…

He looked away so she wouldn't guess at the depth of anxiety that was gripping him. He wouldn't let himself think about any of that now.

The consultant arrived then and, after examining his patient, arranged for her to be checked over by the maternity unit, who insisted on keeping her in overnight.

Late the following day, when the initial scare was over, they released her with the firm instruction that in view of her earlier miscarriage she was to take things very carefully for the rest of her pregnancy.

'Which means giving up anything at all stressful,' Seth remarked as he was driving her back to the apartment. 'Like that high-powered job of yours, for a start.'

'But I can't!' Grace wailed in protest. Because then he would have achieved his ultimate objective, wouldn't he? she thought miserably—seeing her give up her position at Culverwells, the thing he had probably most wanted from the beginning. And because she'd let him get her pregnant with his child!

'You can and you will!' There was no arguing against his decision, because, of course, he could take steps to see that she was removed from the board if she didn't comply.

But he was right in any case, she accepted, praying that this pregnancy would go to its full term. If it didn't, she would lose not only this baby, that she craved to hold in her arms, but Seth as well. Because there would be no reason for him to remain in a loveless marriage—loveless where he was concerned, at any rate, she thought wretchedly—if he no longer felt any responsibility towards her and a non-existent child.

'If you haven't the sense to look after yourself while you're in your condition, someone has to,' he told her with strengthening determination. Which was how, the following afternoon, Grace found herself being whizzed along the motorway in the sleek, dark elegance of his Aston Martin.

'Where are we going?' she enquired as he crossed a myriad fast-moving lanes of traffic that would have made her mind boggle to negotiate, bringing the car deftly and safely onto the carriageway headed west.

'Somewhere where I can keep a closer eye on what you're up to until after our baby's been delivered safely,' he informed her, which was the most information she had managed to get out of him ever since he had instructed her last night on what she should pack.

A couple of hours later, and it all became clear.

Oh, no…

Grace sucked in her breath, recognising the all-too-familiar signs for the little seaside retreat, and sat stiff and tense as the car wound its way onto the quieter road that fringed the rugged coast.

She hadn't been here for over seven long years. Not since her grandfather had sold their holiday home up there in the hills the summer after she had met Seth.

'Relax,' he advised, keenly aware of the tension that was gripping her even as he pulled round a slow farm vehicle. 'I know it's the last place you probably imagined—or wanted—me to bring you, but I promise you'll be comfortable. It's the one place in the world where I come when I want to totally unwind.'

Not a lot had changed over the years, Grace noted as he brought the car down through the town and past the same familiar shops. The little cottage library was still there, and the garage with its one petrol pump, although there was a supermarket now, she noticed, where the general store had been.

'It's scarcely changed,' she breathed aloud, thankful that they had taken a route well away from the boatyard as they came onto the outskirts of the town, because she was battling with so many memories and conflicting emotions that she wasn't sure how to deal with them all at that moment.

'Hasn't it?' Scepticism laced Seth's voice as he put his foot down to take the hill road following the coast and brought the car onto a plot of scrubland at its summit, sending dust and gravel spinning beneath the vehicle's powerful wheels.

Now, sitting there with him high above the sea, as he turned off the ignition she understood why he'd sounded amused, and why he had stopped the car at that particular vantage point.

'I don't believe it!' Grace laughed in shocked surprise.

In the distance, eastwards towards the far side of town, where once acres of derelict industrial wasteland had been, luxury high-rise apartments and prestigiously designed houses stood cheek by jowl around the glistening waters of a new marina graced by cabin cruisers, dinghies and shimmering yachts, whose majestic white masts seemed to pierce the sky. 'What an amazing concept… What foresight someone must have had to create all that…'

'I take it you approve?'

'Who wouldn't?' She exhaled, unable to tear her gaze from the spectacular view. 'So often new developments only ever seem to spoil the environment, but it's been done so sympathetically that I can't see—' She broke off suddenly, aware of the way he was looking at her so intently, of the significance of what he had just said. 'You mean…?' Her eyes were wide with incredulity. 'That whole development—it's one of yours?'

His mouth compressed wryly. 'It was the first.' Though there was pride in his voice as he sat there surveying the result of all that had been conceived out of that brilliant brain, Grace could see the genuine satisfaction in him too. 'But I thought I told you what I was intending to do.'

He had, eight years ago. Shamefully now she remembered how she had laughed, even what she had said in response: *Dreams are for people who crave things they haven't a hope of ever attaining.* How naïve she'd been!

As her disconcerted blue eyes clashed uncomfortably with his, she knew that he was remembering it too.

'It wasn't a dream,' he said softly. 'It was a plan.'

And now he would drive her there, she thought, as the Aston Martin fired into life again. Make her eat humble pie by depositing her in one of those luxury penthouses—which would be a close cousin, no doubt, of the one they shared in London. She could look out at that beautiful marina, at all the boats, houses and everything she had made fun of, unaware then of how much she would wish, every day of her life, that she had never said those things, never treated him as she had. And it would just serve her right! she thought.

Only he didn't.

They were following the coast now, travelling westward,

the road ahead wooded and dropping in a steep gradient into deeper countryside. Below them the water reflected a sky that was a very pale, almost icy blue. Rippling waves left the curve of a shingle beach darkened by the receding tide, while across the estuary, on a road running parallel to theirs, the sun bouncing off a car's windscreen was almost dazzling for a second before the road angled away, climbing upward into the distant hills.

'Did you buy your mother one of those houses back there on the marina?' she enquired, remembering that that had all been part of his long-term plan.

Changing gear, because the road was dangerously bendy, he said, 'She didn't want one. She said that modern places down there were for yuppies, and that she definitely isn't young and most certainly not upwardly mobile.'

Grace laughed at the fond indulgence in his voice and wondered if he would ever speak about her in the same way.

'Nowadays she prefers to live farther north—closer to Alicia.'

'So you were right. Not everything works out the way we plan, does it?' she conceded humbly.

'One learns to compromise.'

As he had by marrying her? Or was she all part of the 'plan' he had referred to just now, as Corinne had suggested she was when she had spoken to her on their return from honeymoon? Either way, it wasn't very complimentary.

'Where are we going?' she asked apprehensively when Seth turned the car off the main highway into a narrow lane. In fact, she already knew.

But why would he bring her here? she wondered desolately. A house that his family had had to move out of because they couldn't afford to stay there. Because of her grandfather. Because of her.

'All right. You've made your point,' she breathed, unable to face seeing the little house—already boarded up that summer she'd last come back here—now gone to rack and ruin. 'I think you've handed out enough just deserts for one day without—'

She stopped in mid-sentence as he brought the car to a standstill in front of a small red saloon that was parked outside the old stone building: a homely looking, picture-book property with gleaming paintwork and shiny windows which were open to the May sunshine.

'You bought it back,' she whispered, tears swimming in her eyes. Not only that, but an extension had been added, in keeping with the rest of the property, providing a whole bank of new rooms along one side.

'Come on.' He was already getting out of the car.

A cacophony of deep barks met them as Seth opened the iron gate to the garden, and Grace caught her breath from a startling *déjà vu* as a chocolate-brown Labrador came bounding down the stony path towards them.

'I don't believe this!' she laughed, surprised. It was like stepping back in time to the night he had brought her here and the Labrador had coming rushing out of the house ahead of Alicia. 'Is it the same dog?' she breathed, flabbergasted. Mocha, she remembered him saying it was called. Because of the chocolate connotations.

'No, Mocha went to her happy hunting-ground some years ago.'

'So what's this one called?' she challenged good-humouredly, petting the animal that was bouncing up and down with excitement, undecided which one of them to bestow the most affection on. 'Crème Caramel?'

'This one's called Truffle,' he corrected, his face alight with pleasure as he ruffled the huge, dark head, unperturbed by the massive paws that were almost on his shoulders with little respect for the casual designer shirt he wore with his jeans.

Grace laughed again, feeling the warmth of his personality,

the strength of his potent attraction as he laughed with her. 'Naturally!' She wasn't imagining it; it struck her suddenly: he seemed more relaxed. Lighter. Different here.

'Seth!'

Grace recognised the pretty copper-haired girl who had come running down the path and was now launching herself into her brother's arms.

'You're obviously missed,' Grace observed, still laughing as she watched him return Alicia's bear-hug, while Truffle did some sort of doggy dance around them, eager not to miss out on his share of the attention.

'Missed?' Alicia wrinkled her nose in mock contradiction as she let her brother go now and treated Grace to a more or less similar greeting. 'I just know which side my bread's buttered!'

She shrieked, darting out of the way of that masculine hand before it could land on her tightly encased, denim-clad bottom.

'Any more talk like that, and you'll be doing without the jam as well,' Seth promised playfully.

'Isn't he tyrannical?' Alicia exhaled, rolling her eyes, seeking mock sympathy from Grace as they started along the path towards the house.

Pulling a face, Grace cast a glance up at Seth and met the sensual challenge in his eyes that dared her to side with his mischievous sister.

'Very!' she laughed without taking her eyes off him, and knew a throb of excitement from the pull of that masculine mouth, that promised that when they were alone together he would make her pay.

The cottage garden, ablaze with flowering shrubs, perennials and fruit trees, complemented the interior of the lovely house. Although retaining many characteristic features in its stone fireplaces, deep-set windows and the odd, strategically exposed beam, it managed to exude modern comfort and convenience in the understated luxury of its furnishings, a blend of the classic and antique.

'So who does Truffle belong to?' Grace asked Alicia a little while later.

The girl had insisted on giving her a tour of the ground floor and showing off the new wing, which comprised a bright and sprawling sitting room and large kitchen which were in total harmony with the rest of the old building.

Apparently, Alicia had only stopped off to stock the fridge on her way to visit her boyfriend in Plymouth, and it was Nadia who had instructed her to leave the dog with her brother.

'I bought him for Seth,' Alicia informed her, ready to leave as they came back into what nowadays served as a dining room in the older part of the house, where they found Seth standing, browsing through an open newspaper on the table. 'I bought him because I thought he needed looking after.'

'Who?' Grace enquired impishly. 'Seth or Truffle?'

'Take your pick.' Alicia giggled, seeming younger suddenly than her twenty years. 'Mum looks after the dog most of the time, though, as Seth doesn't have time to give him all the attention he needs when he's in London. And, apart from that, he's away a lot, so it was a bit of an impulsive move on my part, really.' Something, Grace decided, that Alicia Purvis would be quite prone to.

'You love having him when you're down here, though, don't you, bruv?' she prompted, and was met with a distracted grunt from Seth. With one hand on the back of a chair, one foot on the rung, his dark head bent, idly turning a page, he looked utterly magnificent, Grace thought with her breath catching. 'And having a dog around makes him less of a dynamo and more human like the rest of us,' Alicia was saying. 'Or could it be this house? Again, you'll have to make your own mind up about that. Still, I don't suppose he needs looking after now—now he's got you.'

Propelled into action now, Seth grabbed the soft hat his sister was clutching and with a roguish grin dumped it unceremoniously onto her bright copper head. 'Goodbye, Alicia.'

'Don't let him bully you,' the young woman advised, pulling it straight, darting a glance at Grace from around her brother's lithe and powerful physique. 'If he does, tell Mum. She's the only one he's ever listened to.' And with a shriek, as those keenly honed reflexes made to chase her out the door, his vibrant young sister was gone.

'Is it true?' Grace asked him over the sound of the small saloon starting up.

'Is what true?' He was still wearing that self-satisfied grin.

'That the only person you've ever listened to is Nadia?'

He shrugged, closing the newspaper on the table. 'If I hadn't, I'd have been out of a home—and a good one at that,' he admitted with no pretensions to the contrary. 'At fifteen I was a tearaway with attitude. Someone had to put their foot down or I might well have gone off the rails.'

'She did a very good job,' Grace conceded honestly. 'And your foster father, too.' She remembered him telling her that Nadia had been widowed only a few years after Seth had moved in with them. She guessed, though, that it wasn't only the Purvises' influence that had turned Seth Mason into the self-disciplined, self-sufficient man he was today. He must have wanted to change, or at least to control whatever wild streak he had had. The grit and determination he employed in everything he did and everything he achieved were part of the enduring strength and calibre of his character.

'They knew how to implement just the right balance of understanding, discipline and love,' he told her candidly.

As he would himself with his own child, or children, Grace instinctively decided. With a sudden stab of anguish she prayed that their baby would continue to thrive and grow normally and, when the time came, be delivered safely. She didn't even want to think beyond that.

The upper floor of the house proved to be as full of character and charm as downstairs, although the best room was the master bedroom in the new wing. Spacious and airy, overlooking a private shingle beach, its creamy walls, reflecting the afternoon sun, gave the room a wonderfully golden light.

Behind the king-size bed, dark-rose curtains were tastefully draped from a thick brass pole, blending with the rose-and-cream and brass furnishings in the rest of the room. In the adjoining bathroom a free-standing Victorian bath stood in what seemed like acres of space, surrounded by every modern luxury and amenity for making bath-time pure pleasure.

Seth had gone down for their luggage, but when he returned it wasn't with any of his own.

'Aren't you…?'

'Sharing it with you?' he supplied when she didn't finish her tentatively posed question. His mouth twisted wryly as he set her suitcase down and opened it out for her on the bed. 'I don't think that would be a very good idea, do you?'

Because the doctors had told them that they should be careful?

Just at that moment she didn't care about what the doctors or anyone else had said. *I need you!* she ached to tell him, but kept it to herself.

'If you need me,' he was saying coolly, with no sign of the man who had promised some delightful retribution for teasing him earlier, 'My room's just a stone's throw away.'

Grace nodded, wondering how easy it was for him simply to desert her bed, when inside she craved his love-making more than ever before.

'What else could I need?' she returned with enforced casualness.

CHAPTER TEN

OVER the next few weeks, Grace knew a kind of fragile happiness.

Seth did a lot of work from home, and sometimes when he had to go away he took her with him. She knew, though, from the way she was fussed over by Maisie, the elderly woman who came in to cook and clean on a regular basis, that the woman had been instructed to keep an eye on her whenever he couldn't.

Sometimes he would take whole days off to be with her, and for Grace those were the most precious of all. But there were other times, like now, aching for him, when she would take long walks along the coast with only the sea, the overhead gulls and Truffle at her heels for company.

'It's all right for you,' she told the Labrador as it came running up to her after giving up on a small crab that had disappeared beneath a rock. 'You wouldn't do anything so stupid as falling in love. But I have—and I'm having his baby—and he doesn't even know how much I care about him. You're a dog of the world. Perhaps you could advise me on what I should do?'

Wallowing in all this sudden eye-contact and conversation, the dog jumped up, his big brown nose almost level with her chest, anticipating some exciting treat as well. When a bout of petting was his only reward, he gave a deafening bark and went haring off down the deserted beach, returning soaked to the skin to shake himself violently as soon as he was in drenching distance of Grace.

'Charming!' she laughed, shaking water off her hands. 'What's that supposed to mean? That I drown myself? If that's all the advice you can give, I suggest you keep it to yourself!'

Fondly she stooped to caress the big soggy head before darting out of the way with a little shriek when the dog decided to treat her to another unwelcome shower.

Having just returned from two days of meetings, Seth stopped in his tracks, silencing his barefooted progress across the shingle. It was too evocative a scene to intrude upon, he thought, and stayed there, unnoticed for a few moments, watching Grace with his dog, hoping she wouldn't turn around.

She was wearing a tangerine cotton skirt that floated around her calves like gossamer, and a gypsy-style cream top which she had embellished with a loose string necklace in amber and cream, and a wide matching wrist-band that emphasised her softly golden skin.

With a hand on the burgeoning mound of her midriff that even the loose top couldn't hide now, and her hair—grown long again—blowing softly in the wind, he thought she had never looked so beautiful or so captivatingly maternal as she lifted her other arm to throw a stick for the dog.

Pride was the overriding emotion that rushed over him at the knowledge of this lovely woman being pregnant with his child. But then other emotions rushed in, the least disturbing the surge of hormones that stamped their mark on him as a man, dragging his mind away from those other more complex issues as he strove to bring his body back under control.

She still hadn't seen him; she was still watching Truffle bounding over the shingle. But as the Labrador, stick retrieved, suddenly changed course and raced towards him, she turned around and those precious moments were gone.

Seeing his dark, lean figure advancing along the beach, Grace felt her heart leap like a frisky gazelle.

He had changed before coming out to find her. A white T-shirt hugged the strong contours of his chest, leaving nothing of his magnificent torso to the imagination; his pale-blue denim jeans that encased his powerful legs were frayed at the hems, brushing over feet that were bare and tanned.

'I hadn't seen you as such an animal lover,' he remarked when he was almost level with her, already on his haunches, petting the ecstatic Truffle.

Why was it, Grace wondered, breathless just from the sight of him, that even the sound of his voice should make her heart race?

'You hadn't seen me as a lot of things, including fat and shapeless and undesirable.' Where had that come from? she thought, abashed, adding quickly as grimacing, she tugged at her billowing blouse. 'And unable to get into any of my clothes any more.'

Her words gave him an excuse to visually examine her as he got to his feet.

'There's nothing undesirable about your body being heavy with my child,' he told her dispassionately, with no hint of the need for her that had driven him in the past. 'And your shape will soon come back after it's born. If it doesn't, then I shall take you out and buy you a whole new wardrobe—if it makes you happy. Suits. Dresses. Exotic underwear.'

A fine eyebrow arched dubiously. 'If it makes *me* happy, did you say?'

'All right.' A contorted smile was tugging at his exciting mouth. 'We'll forget the dresses.'

Seeing the mischief twinkling in his eyes, Grace thumped him playfully on the arm. It felt warm and solid, a wall of pure muscle.

'Right!'

She let out a squeal as he made a grab for her, trying to twist away.

'Attack me, would you?'

'No, don't!' she shrieked as she was lifted off her feet, while Truffle, joining in the fun, ran around them, barking hysterically. 'What will the neighbours think?' she protested, clinging to him. Her senses sharpened to the warm softness of his T-shirt, the way his hard body moved beneath it, while his aftershave lotion—still discernible on that darkly shadowed jaw—was sending arrows of want right down through what she thought of as her hippo-proportioned body.

'There aren't any.' Purposefully, Seth carried her over to a small niche between the shallow rocks where he set her on her feet before gently pulling her down beside him on the fine shingle. 'You don't need props to make you excruciatingly desirable to a man. You're too alluring by half—even with the weight of my unborn baby inside you.'

Only not alluring enough for you to love, or make love to, Grace agonised, realising that it had been weeks since he had shown her how much he wanted her—if only sexually, she thought, her pulses suddenly quickening as he leaned over and touched her mouth with his.

It was a mere whisper of a kiss, over too soon when Truffle made his presence felt by clambering all over them.

Grace laughed as a soggy piece of driftwood landed in Seth's lap.

'That dog's going to have to go!' he pretended to threaten. 'I swear the two of you have got some conspiracy going between you.' With enviable strength he hurled the piece of wood farther seawards than Grace ever could have, even from a standing position. 'Go get it, Truffle! See if you can meet the tide!'

'You don't mean that,' Grace chided, laughing again. She

couldn't bring herself to tell him, but she was ecstatic to have him home.

'If it means having my wife to myself for a few minutes, I do,' he said laconically, but the laughter in his face told her he was only teasing. 'Now…where were we?'

'You really think you'll have the chance to find out before he comes back?'

'Is that an evasive answer, Mrs Mason?'

Slipping a hand under her hair, Grace leaned back against the rock with her eyes closed. 'It could be the shortest kiss in the history of the universe.'

'True.'

'It would probably make the Guinness Book of Records.'

'No, that's just the thoughts I've got going through my head right now.'

He hadn't been like this with her since things had started going wrong between them just after their honeymoon: teasing. Tantalising. Playing with her.

'You…!' She couldn't think of an appropriate noun to describe him, and anyway he was leaning over her, his lips tantalisingly close to hers, his breath surprisingly laboured as though he was having some sort of inner battle with himself. One that said he wanted her physically, even while mentally and emotionally she was the last person on earth he would have considered creating a child with, had he but had any choice. 'Ouch!'

'What's wrong?' He drew back sharply on hearing her wince. 'Did I hurt you?'

The concern in his voice made her throat ache, made her realise how lucky the woman would be who he really loved.

'Not you. Your baby,' she admitted, with an inner glow to her face from the beautiful miracle that was unfolding each day inside her. 'It gave one of its stronger than average kicks. It's definitely a boy.'

'You've made up your mind about that, haven't you?' he said, smiling; they had both decided that they would wait until the baby arrived to find out its gender. 'And what's all this unnecessary prejudice I'm sensing against my sex? Can't girl babies do their share of kicking?'

'Of course they can,' she chuckled, her gaze following Truffle who had picked up a scent on the far side of the beach and had happily abandoned his game of throw-and-retrieve. 'But this one's got the boot of a centre forward. Obviously a dominant child who wants to make an impact,' she decided. 'Now, where does he get that from, I… Ouch!'

As another sharp prod had her massaging her swollen middle, the hand that came to rest beside hers was warm and so heart-wrenchingly gentle.

'Can you feel it?' Her mouth was so dry it was difficult getting the words out.

He nodded, those familiar strands of hair moving against his forehead. The pleasure that warmed his features made Grace's heart swell with love for him.

Love me, she ached to say, but she didn't have the nerve.

This wasn't a conventional marriage where they had met and fallen in love, had been desperate to spend the rest of their lives together. This, for Seth, was a partnership he had got himself into out of duty to the mother of his child, and it was just unfortunate that she had been crazy enough to fall in love with him along the way.

'I can't believe how you went through a pregnancy—or halfway through one,' he breathed, 'Before, and I didn't have a clue. Do you know how that makes me feel?'

Grace glanced away, fixing her gaze at some point in the distance where the rocks were turning to gold in the summer-evening sunshine. 'What was the point in letting you know? I scarcely knew you,' she murmured ruefully. 'Anyway, you weren't here.'

'You tried to find me?'

'No.' She sat up quickly, realising she had said too much.

'Then how did you know I wasn't here?'

'My grandfather told me. I didn't know then that the reason he knew about you leaving was that he had got you sacked. But it was the only way I could come back here after my miscarriage.'

'So you did come back?' His face was a contortion of disbelief and something she couldn't quite put her finger on. Horror? she wondered painfully. Was he, in spite of all he had said, wondering what he would have done if she had turned up on his doorstep like a bad penny—not just a stuck-up socialite, as he'd believed she was, but a pregnant one? Putting paid to all his aspirations. His dreams.

'To convalesce,' she enlightened him now. 'My grandparents insisted upon it. I must have been a real pain and a worry to them. I couldn't seem to pick myself up.' She grimaced and, not wanting to sound as though she were courting any sympathy, added with a self-deprecating little laugh, 'Feeling sorry for myself, probably.'

What she didn't tell him, though, was how she had spent those lonely days and nights wandering along the coast, mourning those glorious hours with a man she had found herself wanting more than anything else she had ever wanted in her life, while all the time knowing she had killed all hope of his even liking her—even if she did ever see him again—because of her shameful behaviour.

Caught in the direct line of that steely gaze, she looked quickly away, though not quickly enough not to miss noticing how those thick eyebrows pleated speculatively.

Watching the private emotions that chased across her face, Seth considered what else she wasn't telling him.

'My father sketched me standing next to that rock.' She was pointing to a high ridge where an area of grass clothed the timeless cliffs. She seemed desperate to change the subject.

'Your father?' It came as a surprise to him to hear her mention the man who had deserted her while she'd still been a baby. She seldom did, and he guessed she had only done so now to break the tension between them.

'He came to see me when I was convalescing down here— under sufferance, no doubt, because my grandfather probably demanded it.' She made a cynical little sound down her nostrils. 'It couldn't have been more than a handful of times that he'd been to see me in my life. And you know, he actually asked me to go and live with him that last time. He said he gave me up because he felt it was the right thing to do, but that now I was old enough to make up my own mind. He said he'd come back for me, but then he left and I never saw him again.'

'Did you never think to seek him out? Ask him why?'

The blue eyes that clashed with his were clear and candid. 'Did you, with your mother?'

'Yes. Or at least I tried as soon as I was old enough.'

'What happened?'

'She'd died of a drug overdose the year before.'

Within their frame of gold her flawless features clouded with sympathy. 'I'm sorry.'

There was such intensity of emotion in those two words that he wanted to clasp her to him, bury his lips against her scented hair and lose himself in her tender femininity, in her beautiful body. Not for himself—the man who could scale mountains, remove all obstacles in his path—but for the lost and betrayed young adolescent he had been. But he held back. He wasn't ready to expose himself to such vulnerability.

'Don't be,' he said, getting a grip on himself. 'At least, not on my account. My life turned out well because of Nadia, my foster father, Cory, the twins, and the wonderful family circle I was accepted into. I owe them everything. I couldn't have asked for more. Not for myself.'

'It was pretty much the same for me. It didn't really matter that my father decided to go his own way. My grandparents were great. I didn't need anyone else.' But that wistful note in her voice drew a covert glance from Seth from beneath the heavy fringes of his lashes. She didn't mean that, he was shrewd enough to realise. She might be all bravado up front, but deep down, he suspected, she had felt Matthew Tyler's absence from her life more acutely then she would ever allow anyone to know.

'It's getting late,' he said and catching her hand to pull her to her feet, noticed how cold it was. He gave a shrill whistle that brought Truffle scrambling from somewhere over the rocks towards them. 'We'd best be getting back.'

Her fingers were getting too fat, Grace decided the day she couldn't get her rings on. It didn't make her feel particularly jubilant when the woman who ran the post office referred to her as *'Miss* Mason'.

'One of the drawbacks of being seven months pregnant,' she responded dryly, without really knowing why she felt the need to explain. 'It isn't just the middle bit that swells up!'

It was just that Seth was working such long hours these days, at home and away, that she seemed to be seeing less and less of him, and with the problems they were already facing in their marriage sometimes she felt single as well as unloved. Being forced to discard her wedding band seemed like such an ill-fated thing, she mused now as she sat sketching with Truffle's head resting on her feet under the dining-room table. It was like a curtain closing on a poorly acted scene from a play, a farce, which was what her marriage was. A travesty, she thought torturously, since it would never have taken place had she not been expecting his child.

As her pregnancy progressed, so did her concerns for the baby. Another brief scare when her blood pressure went higher than normal had her constantly worrying that something would go wrong.

Would it come too early? Too late? Would everything be all right?

Her greatest fear was that she would lose the baby altogether, something she couldn't even begin to contemplate.

Nadia came to visit, staying for ten days to be with Grace when Seth had to shoot off to Germany unavoidably on business, and by the time her mother-in-law-left—which, as it turned out, happened to be Grace's birthday—Grace felt considerably better.

'She's done wonders for you,' Seth remarked after they were driving back that day from taking Nadia to the station, a day that couldn't quite make up its mind whether to be blisteringly hot or to cool everyone down with its sudden and unexpected showers. 'It begs the question why you never look that happy and contented when we're on our own.'

'Does it?' Grace murmured, feigning nonchalance. She wasn't going to tell him that she loved him too much to truly let go when he was around for fear of revealing her true feelings for him—not when he didn't love her in the same way—and that sometimes the strain was almost too much for her to bear. 'Perhaps it's because she cooks better than you do,' she added more lightly, although that wasn't strictly true. Nadia was a wizard in the kitchen, but when her son put his mind to it he too could come up with some pretty stupendous dishes.

'In that case,' he said, bringing the Aston Martin through the heavy summer holiday traffic, 'you'll be pleased to know that I'm taking you out for lunch.'

And that turned out to be a four-course meal in her favourite Thai restaurant, which she objected to at first, feeling self-conscious and unattractive in her heavily pregnant state. But Seth had insisted, and she had to admit to having enjoyed it when the lunch was over.

The only down side was having to sit there watching how members of the restaurant's female clientele made no secret of their silent approval of the untamed-looking hunk who was sharing her table, while sparing the odd envious glance at the woman sitting beside him in a sun dress that could have doubled as a tent to see if she measured up.

Now as he was driving her back to the house, sitting there in that silver-grey suit he wore with such mind-blowing style, Grace wondered how she could possibly still be attractive to him when she was waddling around like a lumbering goose. After all, Seth was a sensuous and extremely virile man, yet he hadn't shared a bed with her in weeks.

'You're quiet,' he commented when he was helping her out of the car, the gaze resting on her face softly reflective. 'Are you all right?'

'Of course.' She even managed a little laugh.

The look he gave her as she moved past him told her he wasn't fooled.

'What's the matter?' he pressed when they were inside the house. 'Are you upset because I haven't given you your birthday present yet?'

'Haven't you?' She looked up from petting Truffle, who had nearly knocked her over in his eagerness to welcome her home, her face a picture of mock innocence. 'I hadn't realised.'

He had sent her flowers, though. Red roses, two dozen of them, which had arrived that morning. But what were flowers and presents, she thought achingly, when all she wanted was his love?

'I thought I'd keep something back for later,' he drawled with a flash of something in those incredible steely eyes. 'Something, perhaps, that will show you how beautiful you are. Something you seem to have had difficulty believing lately.'

Unavoidably, her eyes lit up, curiosity breaking through her melancholy mood.

'In the bedroom,' he told her, giving nothing away.

She remembered him coming back inside after he'd handed her into the car earlier with Nadia, and she guessed that that was why.

Frowning, her smile cautious, Grace made her way upstairs.

What did a man like Seth give his wife on her birthday? Something to make her look beautiful, he had said. And in the bedroom.

A sexy nightdress? Enticing underwear?

A leap of reckless excitement was swiftly tempered by unease. He'd said something about that the day he'd come home and found her on the beach with Truffle, but she thought he'd been joking. Would he disappoint her like that?

Gingerly she pushed open the door.

She couldn't see anything unusual at first. There was certainly no exotic clothing spread out on the bed.

A shaft of sunlight slicing through the dark, dramatic clouds broke into the room like a beacon. She followed its path, her head doing a double take as her eyes skimmed over and then returned, shocked and disbelieving, to the figure that graced the top of the bookcase.

Her bronze!

The one she'd always regretted letting go.

She went over to it and ran trembling fingers lightly over the silky-smooth lines of the young woman it depicted, whose blouse hung loosely over her tight-fitting jeans, her long hair blown back by a whipping wind from the sea. Matthew Tyler had captured it all in that lost and lonely look about her. All the turmoil in her face. All the emptiness and lonely longing in her soul.

Hearing the creak of the door, she spun round. Silent tears were trembling on her cheeks.

'Where did you find it?' she whispered.

Seth came in, pushing the door closed behind him. 'You remember the auction?'

How could she forget it? The mixed emotions that had clawed at her that day: the frenetic interest in that saleroom; the escalating bids that had sent the price of her father's work shooting through the roof. The bronze had sold through an agent over the phone on behalf of an anonymous bidder. Someone rich enough and crazy enough to justify spending…

'*You* bought it?' she whispered incredulously.

Beside her now, he ran a hand lovingly over the statuette, just as she had done.

'Why?' Why, when he didn't even like her? she wondered, baffled.

'How could I resist such a work of art?' he said with such a depth of appreciation in his deep voice that she could almost imagine she had heard it tremble.

But why hadn't he resisted it? Because it was a Matthew Tyler sculpture? Or because…?

Her eyelids came down, obliterating the hope that threatened to reveal itself to him, because she didn't think she could really bear to know the answer.

He was a speculator with an eye for an investment. Why else would he have bought it, when his only interest in the girl it represented was to get even with her? While she had gone home, tearing herself apart after the hammer had come down in that auction room for allowing herself to sell it, a decision she had never stopped regretting.

Her eyes clashed with his, her face an open book now. *How had he known?*

'It didn't take much working out to realise how much it had cost you to part with it,' he explained, answering her unspoken question. 'Or why you did.'

'I did it for the money,' she said defensively. 'To pay bills and to save my gallery.' Yet she knew now that, remarkably, it was only Seth's bidding that day that had made it possible. Only *his* money. Nobody else's. So she hadn't been independent from him, even in that.

'Nevertheless…' An arching eyebrow told her that he didn't wholly accept her motives. 'I'm sure if you had had an easier relationship with your father you would have found some other way to raise the money.'

Would she have? Grace bit her lower lip. Possibly. But she had had other grounds for parting with that statue, which were as torturous in their own way as being abandoned by her father.

'Don't be too hard on him for not coming back, Grace. He had his reasons.'

A cloud had crossed the sun again, putting the room in shadow. 'How do you know?'

She saw that broad chest rise then fall after a few moments as he let his breath out slowly.

'Because I made it my business to find out. As big a swine as you think I am, I couldn't stand by and watch you harbouring such hurt and resentment because of the way he deserted you. I found it hard to believe that a man who could create such sensitivity in his work could be so completely without heart. He came from a different background and couldn't fit into your grandparents' world. They didn't want him to marry their daughter, and certainly had no time for him after your mother died. He gave you up, Grace, because they convinced him it was impossible for him to keep you. He believed he was doing the right thing in handing you over and that you'd have a far better life with them than he could ever give you. I had to do some extensive research, but I managed to find out why he didn't contact you again as he promised he would.'

She couldn't believe she was hearing all this. Seth had gone to all this trouble—on her behalf?

'He was a very private person and guarded his privacy jealously, but after a lengthy search I found out from an ex-lady-friend and neighbour of his what happened. He had an accident, Grace, not long after he saw you last. It left him with epilepsy and other problems. She said he didn't want to let you know because he didn't want to ruin your life by making you feel obligated or burdened by him. She said he knew he must have caused you enough pain in your life without causing you any more. Apparently he was banking on the fact that you wouldn't try and contact him, because—as he told his friend and neighbour—he didn't deserve to be contacted.'

And she hadn't, thinking the worst about him.

The tears that had been glistening on her cheeks at having found her most treasured possession now started to flow freely, and suddenly she was sobbing into the warmth of a strong, masculine shoulder.

'I'm sorry, Grace,' he whispered. 'But I couldn't leave you to go through the rest of your life hating him for having broken his promise. His motives were good, even if they kicked in a little too late to do either of you any benefit.'

As her tears subsided he turned her with him to look at her father's work again. 'There's a lot of love in that sculpture,' he observed, running a finger over its fine patina. Because her father had loved her—in his own way. She wasn't in any doubt about that now. 'A lot of love,' Seth reiterated, startling her when he suddenly appended, 'And in more ways than one.'

Could he see it? Had he seen it when he had made that ridiculous bid for it over a year ago? Was it that that had made him buy it?

'I was young. I'd lost my baby.' *And you*, she added silently, but couldn't tell him that.

'Is that all?'

'What else could there be?' she queried, afraid.

He chuckled softly and, reaching out, lifted her chin with a gentle finger. Another shaft of sunlight breaking through the clouds turned his bronzed skin to fiery gold.

'Oh, Grace.' He drew her back to him, his lips against her

hairline so tender that she wanted to weep with the longing for that depth of caring in his voice to mean something. 'You poor, naïve little fool.'

Because, of course, it didn't mean anything—not what she wanted it to mean, anyway. Oh, he would be kind to her. Respect her. Show her all the care and consideration owed to a pregnant wife. But he didn't love her. Wasn't that what he was saying in calling her a naïve fool? Because he must have recognised it on the face of that girl who was immortalised in bronze. One would have had to be blind or stupid not to understand the feelings which her father had captured, the thing which made Matthew Tyler's works stand out over the work of his contemporaries—emotion. And Seth Mason was neither blind nor stupid.

She couldn't resist as his lips moved across her face, her throat, the sensitive hollow at the juncture of her shoulder, and she gave a small murmur of wanting as he slid the thin straps of her dress aside.

Her arms around his neck, she felt his darkly shaded jaw against her cheek, smelled the heaven of his aftershave lotion which, even while it thrilled her, couldn't hide the more potent musk of his own animal scent as he skilfully dispensed with her bra.

Her breasts were heavy in his hands, their large, dark aureoles marking her advanced pregnancy.

Seth groaned as he bent his head to look at her, his hands, his fingers, his touch as reverent as the look of awe that seemed to light his face. Gently then, somehow, they were on the bed, and he was removing the rest of her clothes.

Self-conscious, she uttered a small sound of embarrassment at having him see her naked like this.

'You're so beautiful,' he murmured, and she could see the flush of hard desire, of barely controlled passion, staining his cheeks, a passion that had been stifled and denied them for weeks.

Now it emerged in an urgent fusing of mouths and tongues, and skin against heated skin. He hadn't undressed beyond helping her to remove the shirt she had tugged out of his waistband, so her hands could caress the hair-coarsened contours of his chest and powerful arms, and the velvet-clothed muscles of his back.

Alive and animated with wanting, she could feel the restraint in him, the reined-in passion that he was even now controlling as his lips moved over her face, her neck, her breasts, then down and down, tracing an exquisite path across the most changed and maternal features of her body.

He always had been the most incredible lover, she thought through a drugged and sensuous lethargy, but never more impeccable than this!

Her breath caught sharply at the undeniable pleasure as his lips traced over that most secretive part of her, aware of her need for tenderness, yet aware too of her craving for fulfilment.

Under his consummate mouth, Grace felt a fire starting to build, felt the flames of need leaping and licking upwards through the very core of her femininity until they were too hot to contain, finally exploding in a throbbing inferno that left her sobbing with pleasure, and suddenly gasping with the need for him to stop.

She was so unbelievably sensitive; she couldn't believe how incredibly so as the throes of her orgasm ebbed away. She was too sensitive to be touched any more like that, but she still wanted the one and only thing he could give her—*him*.

Damp, flushed and dishevelled, with a choked murmur of desire she reached for him, but he was already drawing away from her, and a groan of bitter disappointment escaped her when she saw him getting up.

He didn't need her. Not in the way she needed him. Perhaps he had in the beginning, but perhaps he had accepted that that wasn't enough.

'You drive me to distraction,' she heard him whisper, his breathing laboured, but then he left her, and a little later she heard the back door closing downstairs.

Out in the blustery wind, with Truffle at his heels, Seth strode out across the beach, walking off his frustration.

Had it been a mistake, marrying as they had without giving themselves time to get to know each other? He wasn't sure whether, at the time, he'd really known himself whether it was right for the two of them to try to build a life together. He'd only known that he couldn't let any child he'd created suffer in the way that he had.

She'd accused him once, he thought, of marrying her for the doors that she could open for him, and he couldn't deny that in the beginning it had crossed his mind. A sort of added bonus to the knowledge that she was carrying his child. But that was all it had been—a fleeting thought—because he had never needed anything but his own energies and determination to get the things he set his mind on getting. And the one thing he had been determined to get was Grace in his bed on a permanent basis!

But things had backfired on him, things he hadn't envisaged when he had set out to put a wedding ring on her finger. He almost laughed out loud at the way he had thought how smoothly and easily her capitulation to his irresistible charms could be achieved.

She could be in his bed—if he was ruthless enough to forget all that prevented him from exercising that right. But did he want what he had been determined to have—even if he could, without any risk to Grace or the baby—with a whole heap of pride, suspicion and mistrust cooling their bed?

He clicked his tongue for the dog as a squally shower started to blow in off the sea. He only knew that they couldn't go on in the way they were going. Things had changed since the day he had taken her as his bride. Fundamentally changed—for him, at any rate.

After the baby was born, he resolved, gritting his teeth against what he had to do and stepping out against the rain that was already soaking his shirt, he would have to tell her the truth.

CHAPTER ELEVEN

NADIA was fussing around her month-old grandson as if she was the first woman who had ever become a grandmother. The twins, too, had each been to see Grace and Seth at the cottage during the first week of their foster nephew's arrival who, much to their delight had been named Cory—after their father, Seth's foster father—and Matthew, after Grace's father.

'Whatever anyone else does, Seth always has to go one better,' his younger brother, Alvin—who was as every bit as copper-haired and mischievous as his twin sister—had jested, referring to the fact that little Cory Matthew had arrived on the scene weighing nearly ten pounds. 'There should be a law against people like him. You could have killed the girl,' he'd scolded jovially; as everyone had been informed, it hadn't exactly been an easy labour. But then he'd slapped Seth firmly on the shoulder with an unmistakably proud, 'Well done, bro.'

'If ever you need a babysitter, just let me know,' Alicia had begged eagerly, while her mother had wagged a finger in her direction and warned her about getting broody too soon. 'OK, I suppose I won't have much time with my studies,' she'd relented wistfully. 'But while Seth and Grace are looking for a family home nearer London, perhaps now and again I might be able to borrow the dog?'

They had all laughed at that, but Grace had been aware of a distinct unease behind Seth's smile.

Now several weeks on, with the twins having returned to their respective studies, and Cory upstairs in the nursery under the proud supervision of the very capable Nadia, Seth suggested that he and Grace take a drive alone.

'Cory will be fine,' he insisted when she started to express concern over leaving the baby. It was, after all, the first time she had been anywhere without her son. 'Trust me. My mother's an expert at looking after babies,' he said reassuringly and then, his tone turning more sombre, added, 'Grace…we have to talk.'

Something in the way he said that made her stomach muscles clench almost sickeningly. She had known this was coming. She just hadn't realised that it would be so soon.

He didn't say anything as he handed her into the car, not until they were on the tree-flanked road where the turning leaves made a flaming canopy over their heads.

'I think you know why I've brought you out, Grace.'

She glanced at his magnificent figure, casually attired, as she was, in jeans and a light sweater. Looking quickly away again, stalling for time, she said lightly, 'For a drive. Why else?' Her heart, though, was beating wildly and her mouth felt dry.

'Because I think you know as well as I do that things haven't exactly worked out in the way we'd hoped. And that things can't go on in the way they have been.'

'No.' It was a brave attempt to be as practical and realistic as he was.

'Then at least that's half the battle sorted.'

Numbly she uttered, 'I hadn't realised we were fighting a battle.'

He sent her a dubious glance before returning his attention to the road again.

'A cold war—and that's far, far worse.' Deftly he turned the wheel, braking into a bend, before putting his foot down to bring them swiftly yet safely back onto a straight course again. 'I'm sure you'll agree that it isn't a very sound basis on which to build a marriage.'

Achingly she turned away, pulling down the visor to counteract the dappled sunlight that was playing on the windscreen. He'd been different over the past few weeks—no less attentive, yet somehow more distant, preoccupied—although through the long, hard hours when she had been giving birth to his son he hadn't left her side.

'Your family thinks we're very happy. What are you going to tell them?'

'This doesn't concern them.' He brought the car up the steep hill, flicked on the indicator and started slowing down, eventually pulling up on the high area of scrubland where he had parked that day back in the spring when he had first brought her here. 'This is something that only concerns you and me.'

She noticed how the passengers in the car that had been following them glanced back at the Aston Martin as they passed, admiring its low, sleek lines.

'I thought it would be enough,' he stated heavily, turning off the ignition. Something in his voice and the way he sat back on his seat almost with an air of resigned acceptance seemed to squeeze her heart like it was in a vice. 'I thought that expecting and having a child, planning for its future, would be enough to build a relationship on—help us grow together. But it isn't enough, is it, Grace?'

What was he saying? That he wanted out now? It hurt too much even to consider that possibility.

'It doesn't seem to have been, no.' She lifted her chin in defence against the pain, the emotion, that was threatening to overwhelm her. She had to contain it. Stay strong. But how could she when her whole world felt as if it was being torn apart?

'I'm sorry.' His glance took in the rigidity of her pale, tense features, his apology only for the way he was making her feel. 'But I think it's time that one of us, at least, started telling the truth.'

So this was it, the moment she had been dreading, when he explained what it was that had robbed him from her bed. That had taken him away from her—mentally as well as physically—more and more often over the past couple of months, even if he thought she wasn't aware of it. Oh, he had done it discreetly; she had to hand him that. But every woman knew when her husband's attentions were being claimed by something—or someone—else, eventually.

'Who is she?' She couldn't stop herself asking the question, even though she couldn't bear to know the answer and, noticing the line that deepened between the darkening steel of his eyes; she persisted with, 'Who is it, Seth?'

His face was ravaged by some dark emotion she couldn't even begin to comprehend.

'Seth, please…' It was an agonised whisper. 'I've a right to know.'

Seth's breath seemed to shudder through his lungs. 'I suppose you do,' he said in a low voice. Then, surprisingly, he caught her hand, turning it over and studying it intently, as though he were trying to memorise every last detail of its slender, trembling structure.

She didn't trust any man. How could she, he thought, after the experiences she had suffered in the past? She hadn't exactly been ecstatic about getting pregnant and finding herself married to him in the first place, and there had been very little to commend the other men in her life: Paul Harringdale. Lance Culverwell. Her father. So what chance had he imagined there could possibly be for him where the others had failed?

'I suppose,' he said, his voice hesitant, as though he were picking his words carefully. 'I suppose you could say that she's a very special lady.'

Grace closed her eyes. She couldn't, wouldn't, let him see the torture he was putting her through. 'And you're saying you want out of our marriage—is that it?'

His face was slashed with harsh lines. 'Is that what you want me to say? What you've wanted all along?'

She didn't answer. How could he say that?

'I'm well aware that you felt bullied into marrying me. So why did you, Grace?'

'You know why.'

'Tell me. I want to hear you say it.'

She saw his gaze drop to her throat, to the way it worked nervously as she uttered with a painfully disguised version of the truth, 'Because of Cory.'

He nodded, but his face was an inscrutable mask. 'And that's all?'

What did he want her to say? What was he trying to do—wring the truth out of her until there was nothing left? No dignity? No pride? No self-respect?

'No, it isn't, you bastard!' Her chin jerked upwards as she turned away from him. No way was she going to give him the satisfaction of seeing her cry. 'So, now you know.' She was fumbling in her bag for a tissue, but couldn't find one, and when he held out a folded white handkerchief she snatched it from him and blew her nose. 'So, what's she like?' Sightlessly, her eyes were fixed on the boats and waterside apartments way off in the distance. 'This *special* lady.' She couldn't keep the sarcasm out of her voice.

When he didn't answer immediately she sent a guarded look in his direction. Those steely eyes were such dark pools of emotion she felt as though she were drowning in their fathomless depths.

Finally he said, 'Simple. Honest. Uncomplicated.'

It sounded like the echo of something one of them had said a long time ago, but she was too miserable to work out where or when it had been.

'In fact,' he breathed, his tone so velvety-soft that it seemed to brush across her senses, 'I think I can safely say that she's almost as beautiful as you are.'

She couldn't believe he was saying this! Or that she was allowing him to touch her as his fingers strayed across her cheek, tracing the shamefully wet path of her tears.

Even now his touch was unbearably arousing, the scent of his aftershave lotion that still clung to his fingers so achingly dear to her that she could so easily have succumbed to all that he was doing to her, and cried out that she didn't care if he had a thousand mistresses as long as he didn't tear her and their marriage apart like this.

'I really think you should meet her.'

Meet her!

Hurting more than she could believe it was possible to hurt, she pulled back angrily from the dangerous seduction of his touch.

'What the hell are you talking about? What is it you want, Seth—my approval? Or is it my total humiliation you want?'

Quietly, he said, 'It was never my intention to make you this unhappy.' His face was marked with an almost painful intensity. 'I want you to believe that. But I also want you to trust me when I say that what I'm asking of you now is for the best.' His words seemed to tremble from somewhere deep down inside him.

Was that how much he loved her, this woman who was so special to him? At that moment Grace knew a jealousy so fierce that it seemed to consume her.

On a bitter sob, she said, 'Why? To salve your conscience? Haven't you done enough to me already?'

He remained silent for a moment while a nerve started to pulse in that angular jaw.

'I know it might not feel like it to you right at this minute,' he responded at length, taking his keys out of the ignition. 'But anything you think I've done, my love, has all been in your own mind.'

Like expecting her to meet the woman he really loved? Like flaunting his mistress in the way he had flaunted his money, his influence and his power?

A flame of colour surged into her cheeks as bitterly she threw back, 'You set out to destroy me from the beginning. Wasn't that your intention all along?'

His lashes came down as though he were blotting out some truth he didn't want to deal with. But then, exhaling heavily, he admitted, 'In the beginning—yes, I am ashamed to say that I wanted to see you eating humble pie. But then Cory came on the scene—'

'And suddenly your little game of revenge wasn't quite so funny, was it?'

'No,' he murmured, his dark features serious. Contrite, she would have said, if she hadn't felt him incapable of such an emotion. 'It wasn't funny at all.'

Pain corrugated her forehead as she stared out of the passenger window at the red, gold and amber trees that sloped steeply down the hillside, obscuring the tiny bay below.

She'd always known that for him, where she was concerned, all they had going for them was sex. He'd been as driven as she was by the passion that gripped them whenever they came together. But somewhere along the way, while she had fallen deeply and impossibly in love with him, he had met someone else and finally decided that what he had with Grace wasn't enough.

'Come on' she heard him say gently through her darkening despair. 'This isn't doing either of us any good. I think we should take a walk.'

She didn't want to. She didn't have the will or the energy to move, and wouldn't have if he hadn't come round to her side and urged her out of the car.

'Why can't we just go home?' she uttered bleakly, wondering how her legs were going to support her when there was nothing inside her but emptiness.

'Because we both need some fresh air,' he insisted, his hand firm, strong and warm around hers as he tugged her after him down the wooded hillside.

The trees grew thickly in places, and Seth pulled back a branch that encroached over the path so that it wouldn't swing back in her face, his manner caring, at odds with everything that was happening between them. The crisp, dry leaves that had already fallen rustled under their feet, and were still falling—like yesterday's dreams, Grace thought almost unbearably—even as they made their way shorewards.

And suddenly the trees ended and they were stepping out onto the beach, which was protected by a promontory of low rocks immediately to the right of them.

'There,' Seth said softly. 'The lady I want you to meet.' As he spoke it dawned on Grace that they had skirted the headland on their way down through the woods and were standing on the spot where she had come across him on that fateful day all those years before. 'There she is.'

But the beach was deserted, save for a gull that took off with a shriek of protest as their shoes scrunched across the shingle. And the dinghy, on its trailer, just as before.

The sun struck bronze from her gleaming cedar hull and her orange sail was folded neatly against her mast.

It could have been the same sailboat that Seth had been so proud of and which she had practically scoffed at as a spoilt teenager, Grace realised, amazed. Yet she knew it wasn't the same one. This one was new, a replica, lovingly built down to the last detail. But it was the name, painstakingly painted with the same degree of care and loving commitment in gold scripted lettering on the side, that drew the gasp from her lips:

LORELEI

The sea nymph he had likened her to all those years ago!

'She lured me to my fate the day she stumbled upon me on this very beach,' Seth was saying. 'Which was to love her—regardless. Without mercy. Unconditionally. Without any reprieve.'

She couldn't take in what he was saying, nor was she able to speak. Her voice, like her heart, was clogged with so much emotion: shock. Disbelief. Bewilderment.

'I think even you must agree she's a very beautiful lady.'

'Oh, Seth…' As things started to sink in, she found her voice at least. 'Then there isn't…?'

'Isn't what?'

'Anyone else?' She felt as though she was on an emotional rollercoaster, first down, then up, up so high that she felt dizzy from the heights to which she was being driven.

'Why does that surprise you so much, Grace? Haven't you realised yet how much I love you?'

Her heart swelled until she thought it was going to burst, her mind still unable to grasp that he was actually admitting to loving her. 'But I thought…'

'You thought what? That I'd even want to look at another woman after being with you?' Seeing her shake her head with incredulity, that look of amazed incomprehension still etched on her face, he went on, 'What is it going to take, Grace? A full admission—that I fell in love with you so long ago? That

that was what kept me driven and made me so determined to make you pay for shunning me in the way you did?' His grimace was self-deprecating. 'Although I didn't fully realise that that's what it was until I started to get to know the real Grace Tyler for myself.'

She bit her lower lip to try and contain the joy that was oozing through every last part of her, unable to quite believe that she could be the only woman in his heart—this man she adored with her whole being, with her very life.

'But you forced us to stay apart. Sleep in separate rooms. You haven't even wanted to touch me for goodness knows how long,' she added, hurting as she remembered it, and feeling surprisingly shy, in the light of having recently supplied him with a big, beautiful baby son.

'Oh, I wanted to. Believe me, I wanted to!' he stressed fervently, expressing all the torture it had cost him to exercise such restraint and self-denial. 'But it was the only way I could trust myself to keep my hands off you. After what had happened to your mother and all the problems you suffered, first with your miscarriage and then carrying Cory, I didn't want to do anything that would endanger your life or the life of our baby. I wasn't prepared to take any chances, and I knew I'd only wind up making love to you if I shared your bed.

'I also thought that it wouldn't do us any harm to cultivate some other aspects of our relationship—like trust and openness and friendship—without our very pleasurable but uncontrollable need for each other swamping everything else that we should have been sharing. I didn't consider that in doing so I was just pushing you further away from me. But I wanted you—loved you—from the moment that I first laid eyes on you in that boatyard—a haughty little snob who couldn't fight what was happening between us no matter how much she might have wanted to.'

'Was that why you bought my statue?'

'What do you think?' he said. With a wry twist of his mouth, he added, 'Although at the time I felt it gave me some kind of advantage over you to own it. But why did you sell it? It wasn't just because you didn't want to keep anything of your father's, or to get out of a financial fix, was it?'

She shook her head. Now wasn't the time for holding anything back.

'It always made me unhappy to look at it, because of the time in my life that it reminded me of. I'd treated you so badly and I was so sorry for that. When I lost the baby, the one thing that had come about because of that beautiful time we had together—and it was beautiful, no matter what I wanted you to think at the time—I thought I was being punished. And in a way I was, because that miscarriage brought home to me what was valuable in my life and what wasn't—and it certainly wasn't any of the material things I'd thought were so important to me. I knew that what *you* had were the things that really mattered—candidness. Integrity. Being true to yourself. When I thought I'd killed all those things I'd respected about you, I can't tell you how unhappy that made me.'

Lovingly she ran a hand over the gleaming gold name of the siren he had compared her with in the beginning. 'But I hadn't, had I?' she murmured wistfully. He was still the same man she had met what seemed a lifetime ago now: ambitious. Energetic. Driven. But also compassionate and tender. She liked to think, though, that she wasn't the same girl. Or at least she hoped she wasn't.

His eyes followed the slender fingers that were tracing his handiwork before he covered her hand, his fingers interlocking with hers.

'What do you think?' he breathed, pulling a wry face.

'I think I love you,' she whispered, with all the feeling in her heart, and gave a small gasp as he caught her to him.

So much time, so much love, had been wasted because

of her pride—because of his, he thought. But he intended to change all that, starting from now.

'I'll take you out in it some time,' he murmured breathlessly, alluding to the little boat he had built for her, when they finally managed to come up for air, reluctantly breaking from their desperately impassioned kiss. 'But first I need to get home and persuade Nadia that Cory and Truffle could do with some fresh air and exercise, and a bit of human-canine bonding. Because right now, Mrs Mason, I really need to avail myself of the long-awaited delights of my wife's bed.'

Excitement leaped in her as he urged her back towards the car. She hadn't imagined she could be so happy and wondered by what miracle it had all come about.

A couple of hours later, lying in his arms in the beautiful bedroom from which he had once exiled himself, she noticed him looking up at the bookcase and the figurine.

'You called me naïve and a fool that day you gave it to me,' Grace reminded him a little reproachfully, still wondering why he had said it. 'I thought it was because you realised I loved you even then, and that I still did, and that you were feeling sorry for me.'

He laughed indulgently at that. 'I must confess I started to suspect how you felt about me then, but I didn't dare hope for too much. But I called you a fool, my love, for destroying what we could have had from the beginning—and naïve because you let social differences stand in our way. I wanted to tell you how I felt that day—on your birthday—but you didn't trust me enough to talk about your feelings, and I was afraid that I might have been imagining what I wanted to believe. All I hoped was that, if I could do enough to show you how much I cared, you might eventually realise how much I loved you.'

And he had, Grace realised. In so many ways. He'd given

her everything she had ever wanted, that she could ever want: in his child; in a gentler view of her father the day he had surprised her with that figurine; with the boat this afternoon. He'd also saved the company, because shares had rocketed over the past couple of months, and he'd guaranteed her a seat on the board whenever she wanted to return.

'When I discovered I'd been your first lover, I can't begin to tell you how that made me feel. But the thought of another man holding you like this, making love to you—' his deep voice shook with something close to anguish '—when it should have been me…'

'There was only ever you,' she murmured against the dark strength of his throat, desperate that he should know that, and realising how much it would mean to him to be told.

'You mean…?' From the way his voice tailed off and those powerful arms tightened around her, she knew he was totally overwhelmed by her admission. 'You should have let me know,' he breathed at length. 'Opened up to me. Although I knew you'd never admit to loving me, that you didn't trust any man enough to allow your feelings to be exposed so completely.' He paused, then added, 'Which was why I forced you into it in the way I did this afternoon.'

'So it was all a ploy!' She thumped him on his deep bared chest, feeling the thrill of his strength, the solidity of velvet-clad muscle that made her heart race as she remembered how tenderly he used that strength in making love to her. Never had she imagined she could be so happy, or as lucky as to be given a second chance with this wonderful man. But she was, she thought ecstatically, because she knew now how much he loved her, and she also knew that she was worthy of that love. And unlike the other men she had known—Paul, her father, her grandfather—she knew instinctively that this man she cared for more than anything else in the world was never going to let her down.

'I know I should have trusted you.' She brought herself up on an elbow. 'Told you how I felt.' Lovingly she brushed back the familiarly loose strands of hair from his forehead.

'Then tell me now.'

'I love you,' she murmured, lowering her lips to his, and then, rolling on top of him, set out to prove it in the most pleasurable way she knew.

MODERN

SHAMEFUL SECRET, SHOTGUN WEDDING
by Sharon Kendrick

Shop assistant Cassie Summers agrees to be international playboy Giancarlo Vellutini's mistress for Christmas... But will an unexpected gift make this temporary arrangement last a lifetime?

SCANDAL: UNCLAIMED LOVE-CHILD
by Melanie Milburne

Billionaire Luca Sabbatini may have ruthlessly cast Bronte from his life, but he hasn't forgotten the sweet ballerina. He's ready to reawaken their lost passion – however, the secret she's hiding will have its repercussions!

HIRED BY HER HUSBAND
by Anne McAllister

When Sophy wakes up and realises her marriage to George Savas is a sham, she never looks back. But when stubborn and proud George wants her help, he soon realises that his need for Sophy runs deep...

A MISTAKE, A PRINCE AND A PREGNANCY
by Maisey Yates

Eternally single Alison Whitman is carrying the *royal heir* of the Prince of Turan! Maximo will seize this surprise chance at fatherhood, but he'll never stand for an illegitimate heir...

On sale from 1st October 2010
Don't miss out!

Available at WHSmith, Tesco, ASDA, Eason and all good bookshops

www.millsandboon.co.uk

2 FREE BOOKS
AND A SURPRISE GIFT

We would like to take this opportunity to thank you for reading this Mills & Boon® book by offering you the chance to take TWO more specially selected books from the Modern™ series absolutely FREE! We're also making this offer to introduce you to the benefits of the Mills & Boon® Book Club™—

- **FREE home delivery**
- **FREE gifts and competitions**
- **FREE monthly Newsletter**
- **Exclusive Mills & Boon Book Club offers**
- **Books available before they're in the shops**

Accepting these FREE books and gift places you under no obligation to buy, you may cancel at any time, even after receiving your free books. Simply complete your details below and return the entire page to the address below. You don't even need a stamp!

YES Please send me 2 free Modern books and a surprise gift. I understand that unless you hear from me, I will receive 4 superb new books every month for just £3.19 each, postage and packing free. I am under no obligation to purchase any books and may cancel my subscription at any time. The free books and gift will be mine to keep in any case.

Ms/Mrs/Miss/Mr _____ Initials _____

Surname _____

Address _____

_____ Postcode _____

E-mail _____

Send this whole page to: Mills & Boon Book Club, Free Book Offer, FREEPOST NAT 10298, Richmond, TW9 1BR

Offer valid in UK only and is not available to current Mills & Boon Book Club subscribers to this series. Overseas and Eire please write for details..We reserve the right to refuse an application and applicants must be aged 18 years or over. Only one application per household. Terms and prices subject to change without notice. Offer expires 30th November 2010. As a result of this application, you may receive offers from Harlequin Mills & Boon and other carefully selected companies. If you would prefer not to share in this opportunity please write to The Data Manager, PO Box 676, Richmond, TW9 1WU.

Mills & Boon® is a registered trademark owned by Harlequin Mills & Boon Limited. Modern™ is being used as a trademark. The Mills & Boon® Book Club™ is being used as a trademark.